C000242385

STRESSED ERIC's

Guide to Stress MANAGEMENT

STRESSED ERIC's

Guide to Stress MANAGEMENT

Eric Feeble

This book is published to accompany
the television series entitled *Stressed
Eric* which was first broadcast in 1998.
The series was produced by Absolutely
Productions Limited in association with
Klasky Csupo, Inc for the BBC.

Created by Carl Gorham

Executive producers: Miles Bullough, Claire Jennings, Gabor Csupo and Arlene Klasky

Creative producer: Stig Berquist

Written by Carl Gorham and Michael Hatt

Design by DW Design, London

Illustrations by James Mayall

Published by BBC Worldwide Ltd, Woodlands, 80 Wood Lane W12 0TT

First published 1998

© Carl Gorham & Michael Hatt 1998

The moral right of authors has been asserted

ISBN 0 563 38446 8

Printed and bound in Great Britain by Butler and Tanner Limited, Frome and London

Cover printed by Belmont Press, Northampton

Contents

Why I wrote this book

A friend of mine who works in publishing asked me if I'd like to get involved in a book about stress. As a member of the public with, as he put it, considerable experience in the field, he felt I was uniquely placed to advise him on the management of stress in modern life. What started out as a collaboration with me as mate-to-occasionally-bounce-ideas-off-in-idle-moments-down-the-pub ended up as a solo project with me as researcher-editor-writer-person-who-decides-which-kind-of-glue-to-use-in-the-binding. The reason for this was that Mark was forced to devote all his time to several of the more troubled titles on his autumn list, namely, *The History of the Sewing Machine* and *Greenland in Pictures*.

I won't bore you with the stressful nature of becoming a first-time author two and a half weeks before the date of publication, but I should say for anyone contemplating doing the same, you can get similar results from suffering a bereavement, moving house and getting a divorce all on the same day. I don't blame Mark. It's hard to blame someone when they're spending most of their time either crying, dribbling or under heavy sedation. I wish him all the best and hope that a short spell in Gresty Fennels Drying-out Clinic near Farnborough will give him the fresh start he so badly needs.

As for myself, Doc says he doesn't think I should get involved in another book for the foreseeable future. By the time I finished this one, my blood pressure was in the region of 280 over 130, which is normally found only in people experiencing a heart attack. He has advised me to rest and take a little light exercise. This has taken the form of some extremely uncompetitive games of tennis with my son, Brian, who has yet to return my serve in over 140 attempts.

In the meantime, I do hope you enjoy this book. I certainly didn't.

Eric Feeble

Acknowledgements

My thanks to Doc for prescribing me enough Xangadanthine and Anti-hestaglorine to see me through. Thanks also to my boss, Paul Power, for kindly agreeing to provide a preface. No thanks at all to either my ex-wife Liz who, in a fit of pique, tore up my original notes and recycled them into eco-friendly place mats, or to the au pair, Maria, who used an early version of the introduction to wipe her bottom.

Lewisham Single Fathers Suffering From Skin Disorders Support Group (LSFSFSDSG) also deserves a mention, as do the Au Pair Crisis Line, Deptford, and HOPELESS!, a new mutual aid network for parents with under-achieving children.

Also not to be forgotten, Mrs Hettie Johnson, the most enthusiastic librarian I've ever met and someone who, despite her deafness and dyslexia, was a sterling ally during a troubled research period. I also benefited enormously from discussions with Martin and Elizabeth Gentleriver (née Smayles) and their lovely daughter Summer Solstice from the Palmers Green New Age Healing Centre. Many thanks to them, as well as to their colleagues Cloud, Sparrow, and Wind-in-the-Hair.

Finally, my greatest thanks go to my children, Claire and Brian, for being so patient (if, in Brian's case, totally unaware of what he was being patient about). Claire's enthusiasm for the project never wavered, and I shall always remember the look of excitement on her little face when she received an advance copy of the book. What a tragedy, then, that she turned out to be allergic to the cover. My love to you, darling, and everyone else on Simmonds Ward. Fingers crossed you'll be home for Easter.

8

Preface

by Paul Power

Chief Executive, Power Enterprises plc

When I was asked by Feeble to write a few words in the front of his book, I agreed. Usually, these prefaces are a load of congratulatory arseburgers spouted by some sycophantic sap desperate to lift the whole enterprise off the crapper and into the bath. But I'm not like that. I'm a blunt man and I speak as I find, and I'm not going to pretend I like something when I really think it's about as worthwhile as a condom in a sperm bank. So here's what I think.

Stress is for social workers and dagos. It's not for me. After all, do I want to read about anxiety and worry and someone getting the squitters every time they have to change a light bulb? Do I, arseburgers! I want to read about being in control, about being in charge, about being a leader of men. In short, I want to read Ray Perfect's *Health, Wealth and Happiness* published by Splendid Books at only £25.99, to which I've also contributed an introduction. It's a triple-decker arseburger of a book with extra cheese, mayo and delicious soft beverage of your choice. It's got colour pics, pull-outs, advice, laughs and stunning truths from the four corners of the globe. You can scratch it, you can sniff it, you can pop it up, you can stick it on the coffee table and amaze your next door neighbour so much that he'll let you have sex with his wife. This book, on the other hand, is a depressing whinge. It's probably okay if you've got a lot of time on your hands, as in a major air traffic control strike or a long-term hostage situation, but even then it might be more fun counting to 12 million.

Arseburgeringly yours

Paul Everest Strongbow Power

What is

Stress?

tress is probably one of the most common ailments afflicting people today. Survey after survey bombards us with statistics about how stressed we are as a nation. This in itself causes stress. For instance, while reading a recent report, I came across this statistic:

84% of people in the United Kingdom claim to be suffering from some sort of stress.

Now, I don't wish to appear overly cynical, but let's examine this statistic more closely. First of all, who are these 84% of people? Where do they live? Apparently this survey was based on a 'representative sample of 128 people'. Maybe I'm missing the point, but it seems to me that 128 is hardly representative of a population of over 54 million. It's barely representative of the population of Dartford.

Besides, what kind of people stop to talk to researchers, anyway? I'll tell you what kind of people: sad, lonely, often one-step-away-from-going-out-in-their-pyjamas people. No wonder they're suffering from stress.

Anyway, it's probably completely made up. How often have you been stopped by someone asking about your stress levels? The only people who ever stop me are either Hare Krishnas, smarmy blokes trying to sell me insurance, or lost French tourists looking for the coach station.

What people often forget is that stress is necessary to human existence. In small doses it sharpens our reflexes, heightens our responses, and enables us to cope with demanding and difficult situations. Here is a graph, illustrating the correlation between the amount of stress and its positive or negative effects on human behaviour during an important and stressful event (a high-powered job interview).

STRESSED
ERIC

Quality of your Performance

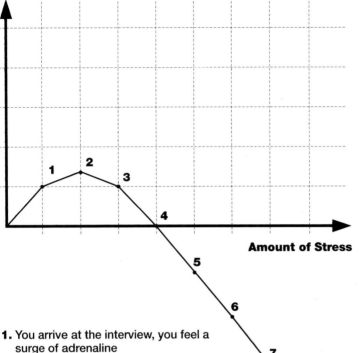

Amount of Stress

1. You arrive at the interview, you feel a surge of adrenaline

2. Your conversation is sharp and precise

3. Your conversation is less fluent, but nonetheless focused and improved

4. Your conversation is starting to run out and you're filling the conversation with lots of ums and ahs

5. The ums and ahs are now high pitched and continuous and you sound like Norman Wisdom

6. You'd give anything to sound like Norman Wisdom

7. Plenty's coming out of your mouth now, but it's all dribble

8. You dream of a time when all that was slackening was your conversation

9. You evacuate in front of the board of ICI

A Brief History **of Stress**

The following section is, by necessity, incomplete. I was unable to finish my research because the local library, in common with many under-funded London libraries, now operates the following opening hours:

	morning	afternoon
Monday	closed	2 pm – 4 pm
Tuesday	closed	closed
Wednesday	closed	closed
Thursday	closed	closed
Friday	11 am – 12 am (March to September)	closed
Saturday	closed	closed
Sunday	closed	closed

In addition, borrowing books was out of the question. My ticket allows me to borrow four books at a time, and I am currently unable to return the four I have out, for the following reasons:

1. Joan Baez, **My Struggle** – defaced by Maria with the words *'che lo lomero que la hippy shit'*

2. **The Boys' Book of Constructive Things to Do** – which Brian has very constructively chewed into the shape of a Polo mint

3. **Coping with Extreme Allergies** – Claire was allergic to the dust jacket and was sick all over it

4. **The Case for Mercy Killing** – used by Maria to mop up the sick on *Coping with Extreme Allergies*

STRESSED ERIC

I therefore tried illicit borrowing by slipping some books down through a hole in the pocket and into the lining of my overcoat, but this unfortunately came to grief. Mrs Johnson, the librarian, though deaf and dyslexic, isn't blind, and the sight of a man in a completely rigid coat aroused even her muted alarm bells. I apologize to her for any embarrassment caused and would like to thank PC Wilkinson for being sympathetic enough to pretend he believed me when I told him I was an English teacher working at a non-grant-aided day centre for Albanian refugees.

Consequently, the research was limited to what could be achieved during the three hours a week that I could actually get into the library. My research was further hindered by an early misunderstanding concerning the nature of my work. Mrs Johnson was extremely enthusiastic and kind and directed me to important books, all of which were, somewhat puzzlingly, in the opera section. It was only after two weeks of rather baffled study that I realized she had misheard me and thought I was writing a book about Strauss.

So here is what I've been able to achieve given the Charge-of-the-Light-Brigade-type odds against me.

The Prehistoric Era

Compared to the fundamental necessities of life, such as finding the next meal and not being eaten on your way to school, practising the Alexander technique is undoubtedly a luxury. But that is not to say that stress, or an awareness of stress, did not exist in prehistoric times. After all, what could be more stressful than being chased through a peat bog by something hungry the size of Poland? It's unlikely that cavemen had a word for stress (it's unlikely that they had a word for very much) and we certainly don't see any pale, gaunt, chain-smoking men in cave paintings, but this doesn't mean that it wasn't on their minds.

And what was the Ice Age about? It was about being cold the whole time. And the Bronze Age? They must have been so sick of bronze by the end of it. Then there's the Stone Age, the Iron Age – all these ludicrously one-track ages. We live in such a rich and balanced environment, we all too easily forget how stressful it must have been living in a world that lurched from one crude new technology to another. And what about all the ones we haven't heard about that didn't succeed? Was there a very short-lived Feather Age, when people tried to build their homes out of feathers? Was there a very unsuccessful and unpopular Manure Age (there would have been plenty of it), when people tried to make weapons out of manure?

Prehistoric man armed with dung crossbow.

STRESSED ERIC

The Romans

The Romans were much more civilized than anything that had gone before, but civilization brings with it new stresses. A highly developed society has much greater expectations, but these are not always easy to fulfil since technology rarely keeps pace with aspiration. For instance, the Romans might have wanted to construct great civic buildings, but how do you build them when you don't have any proper cranes? As someone who has trouble assembling a flat-pack wardrobe from MFI, the thought of building Hadrian's Wall when all you've got is huge lumps of stone and a lot of grumpy slaves brings me out in a rash.

This is typical of the Roman era as a whole. In many respects they were so advanced, and yet in others they were a bunch of village idiots. They had magnificent buildings, spas, laws, currency and baths, but they had absolutely nothing to offer in the way of trousers. It seems to have been skirts all the way, male or female, summer or winter. Can you imagine patrolling Hadrian's Wall in a mini-skirt? Fighting in a mini-skirt? Getting married to someone-in-a-mini-skirt in a mini-skirt?

People also credit the Romans with inventing the lavatory. For anyone involved in this process, it must have been more stressful than all the wall-building and skirt-wearing rolled into one. Imagine this: you wake up on Monday morning and realize you have to spend another long week in the Lavatory Research Centre. Day after day, you try to work out how to make the contraption flush properly. And then, when you do get it to flush, you have to make sure it doesn't all come back again twenty seconds later. What a nightmare!

When they did finally create the toilet, it was completely communal. I don't know about you, but when I go to the loo I can't go in front of someone else, so I always use a cubicle even when I'm just having a wee. In fact, I'd prefer it if the cubicle was hermetically sealed and soundproofed (but that's another issue). So, imagine having to do everything in public, which means quite possibly in front of your children, your mother-in-law and the Roman equivalent of the vicar. I wouldn't have been able to go at all. I would have had to hold on until the Saxon Era.

The **Middle Ages**

In the Middle Ages, did they look back at the Romans and think: 'Where's it all gone? Where have the banks, postal services, laws, baths, spas, nice buildings and central heating disappeared to? How come they had all that stuff 800 years ago, when we're now living in crappy houses made of wattle and daub, sleeping on straw and eating turnip peelings?' If they did, and someone must have done (even allowing for the general level of medieval gormlessness), then it must have been staggeringly stressful. It takes me days to recover when I lose the key to the front door. Imagine how much worse you'd feel if you'd lost the key to civilization.

But the most stressful thing by far about the Middle Ages was that everyone was incredibly violent. People were constantly going to war with each other over the least thing. Take the Wars of the Roses. When you analyse it, this was really a war about which side of the Pennines you came from. Imagine having to fight somebody just because they came from Altrincham. My research revealed that the only way they were able to distinguish between friend and foe was by each side wearing either a red rose or a white rose. Now how practical is that?

Die, red-rosed fiend

It's white. I just got blood on the petals

STRESSED ERIC

The Elizabethan Age

When people talk about the Elizabethan Era, they describe it as a time of great cultural flowering, when science, the arts and exploration all blossomed. They claim that court life was the epitome of elegance and refinement, full of great wits and beauties engaged in urbane conversation and intellectual enquiry.

This is so far wide of the mark, it's hard to know where to begin. What the Elizabethan Age really offered was a hitherto unimaginable range of high-stress situations and possibilities for extreme anxiety.

Take the arts. Shakespeare, our greatest ever playwright, is the symbol of Elizabethan culture. I don't know about you, but I find it bad enough going to a Shakespeare play now – four hours of being spat on by some punchable drama school graduate shouting at the top of his voice, never mind the fact it's only you and his mother sitting in the audience. In 1603, you wouldn't even have been able to sit down. And after standing through one of those interminable plays where everyone's named after a town in the Midlands, you'd file out in the pitch dark (no street lighting) only to be set upon by a gang of yobs with terrible teeth.

As for court life, being a courtier must have been one of the most stressful occupations in history. Success depended entirely on looking fashionable, being in favour and generally licking the Royal Behind. However, this was no easy feat. For one thing, no one ever changed clothes. You were simply sewn into your kit for a year. Imagine if, one week after being imprisoned in your new day-glo doublet and hose, the damn thing went straight out of fashion and you had to spend the next 51 weeks being the laughing stock of all London.

The Spanish Armada

The Spanish Armada struck me as another extraordinarily worrying event. By some distance, the most ridiculously stressful bit must have been Drake's insistence on finishing his game of bowls before dealing with the Armada. How tense-making must that have been for everybody who was standing around the edge of the bowling green saying, 'Bravo, Drake! Truly is he a noble and proud leader,' while thinking, 'Oh, my God, hurry up, you stupid bastard.'

Another thing to note about the Armada is the fact that more people died on the British side through food poisoning than through fighting. How stressful is that? You spend all day risking life and limb for your country, miraculously dodging cannonballs, musket fire and whirling swords, you get back to camp exhausted and starving and then get kiboshed by a dodgy piece of salami. The single biggest loss of life during the Armada – some 800 men in a three-day period – was due to an outbreak of food poisoning in the British camp at Tilbury, and all because of some bad sandwiches. True, your average Elizabethan would have been pretty philosophical about death, given the widespread infant mortality, gangrene and influenza, but even they would have been pretty pissed off at being killed by dinner.

STRESSED
ERIC

The Age of Reason

What struck me about the Age of Reason were the great anomalies that sudden huge advances in science throw up. Not unlike the Romans, it's another troubling mixture of knowledge and ignorance. Imagine being Isaac Newton. You get home and you've had a profoundly great day. An apple has fallen on your head and you've made a discovery that's going to influence the world for centuries to come. You sit down when you get in and you think, 'I still smell like a turd sandwich.' Don't be silly, I hear you say, he didn't notice – they didn't then. Did he really not notice? Did this man, with his brain, ability and insight, not have sufficiently developed nostrils to sense that he whiffed something in the order of a vat of sulphur? I don't believe you. Maybe it was a conspiracy. Maybe Newton had severe doubts about his own pungency and everyone just lied to him.

Historical Encounter *(heavily recreated)*

> **Newton:** *Is it just me, or am I humming up a storm?*
> **Friend:** *Can't smell a thing.*

But then you'd hardly reckon on the man who discovers gravity not having a mind of his own, would you? Or being easily persuaded, against his better judgement, that he smelt of lilac when he in fact smelt like a pig had died in his underpants.

Historical Encounter *(again heavily recreated)*

> **Newton:** *Is it just me, or am I humming up a storm?*
> **Friend:** *Can't smell a thing.*
> **Newton (Angrily):** *I've just discovered gravity. Do you think I don't know my own nostrils?*

So if he wasn't stupid and wasn't gullible, Newton must have realized he smelt terrible. And for a man who could conquer the seemingly insoluble questions of the Universe, it would have been a terribly stressful psychological moment to realize he still couldn't stop himself whiffing like a cowpat.

Nelson

Nelson was a great leader, a hero, a noble warrior and a patriot. But he was also a Grade A stress-giver. And why? Well, without being disablist about it, we all know he had one eye. Now, that's not an insurmountable problem I admit, but when your entire job is about judging the distance between two very large lumps of ship, being one short in the eye department is not going to inspire confidence. I don't know about you, but if I shut one eye, I can't get my thumbs to meet. Nelson, remember, was in charge of the entire British fleet. Even allowing for his superb military record, charisma and social standing, if I had been standing next to him when he issued the order, 'Board!' about a ship three miles away, I'd have been forced to ask, 'Are you absolutely sure about that?' Hardy must have had a hellish time, running round, reinterpreting everything Nelson said in order to stop the entire crew hurling themselves into the sea. At the same time, he had to ensure that no one thought he was being insubordinate or disobeying Nelson. What a complete heart-attack situation. And to top it all, the famous death-bed kiss must have sent Hardy close to a full coronary – imagine having to snog your boss in front of everyone.

STRESSED ERIC

The Victorian Era

The Victorian Era is well known for many things: great industrial advances, the construction of railways, bridges, whole cities, great novels, but perhaps the thing it's best known for is hypocrisy. Now, hypocrisy is stressful. It's very difficult to do or say two things at once (I find it difficult to do one thing at once). It takes twice the energy and twice the effort, especially when the two things are exact polar opposites. Being an average, pious, church-going Victorian gentleman would have been highly stressful as you went from temperance meeting to prayer service to Madame Sponkin's house in Great Titchfield Street for a quick spot of trampolining with Big Ida.

What was particularly stressful about leading this hypocritical double life was the constant fear of discovery. It was quite possible that Big Ida might be saved by the local vicar and turn up at the next prayer meeting. It would have been entirely in keeping with Victorian hypocrisy if she'd turned out actually to *be* the local vicar. It was also quite possible that your wife might have suspected something, given your lateness for dinner on Thursdays, the faint aroma of cheap scent on your frock coat or, perhaps the most telling clue of all, your premature death from syphilis. But then the Victorian Era was all about repression, deceit and the refusal to discuss real issues.

The Victorians also suffered enormous stress because the sheer pace of change was so much greater than anything that had gone before. The resulting difficulties were so much bigger, the teething problems so much more massive. London went from being a small town to the biggest city in the world in a couple of decades, yet it still had no proper drinking water, sanitation or street lighting. Not only were you forced to live in a squalid, smelly single room in an overcrowded tenement building, but you couldn't find your way back to the bloody thing at night. Even the graveyards were overcrowded, with most people having to share graves. One writer describes seeing the silhouetted figure of a gravedigger jumping up and down on the bodies in one grave, trying to pack them down like clothes in a suitcase that won't shut. We are told that those people who work in the bereavement industry today suffer a special kind of stress from being surrounded by dead bodies all the time. It must have been so much worse when you had to jump up and down on them as if they were your wife's cardigans.

Some Other Stressful **Historical** Events

The Vikings

Historians often remark that it would have been very stressful being a victim of the Vikings' raping, pillaging and looting. But no one ever considers how stressful being a Viking must have been if you were gay, vegetarian and pacifist.

The Exploration of the New World

One thinks of the obvious stresses, such as hostile native people, wild animals, disease – but what about packing? Packing must have been a nightmare. How do you know what to pack when nobody's been there before and no one can tell you what the weather's like? There won't be a porter or a trolley when you arrive, so you can't take too much, and you've no idea how long you're going for because you don't know how far it is.

The Great Plague

Not only have you got a horrible embarrassing anti-social affliction, but everybody gets to know about it because they put a huge red cross on your door.

The Charge of the Light Brigade

They must have known very, very, very early on that this wasn't a good idea. They must have. Even allowing for the traditional stupidity prevalent in the British Army, even allowing for the gross lack of imagination that reveals itself in things like the Royal Tournament, there must have been at least some people who thought right from the outset, 'Horses, cannon, cannon, horses. You're kidding, aren't you?'

Custer's Last Stand

Stressful, but not as stressful as Custer's Second-to-Last Stand, which must have happened shortly before the last one. It would have been like the last one, except they must have won, only to be told at the end, 'you're doing the same thing next week'. Now that's stressful.

The First Aeroplane

If they were the first to take to the air, where did the Wright Brothers get insurance?

The Discovery of Radium

There it is, in the sink for the first time. First of all you think, 'Oh great, I've discovered a highly powerful new element.' But then, don't you think straight after, 'Oh help, there's something radioactive in the washing-up bowl'?

The Second World War

Chock full of stressful things. Being given one of those useless air raid shelters that went under the kitchen table rather than in the garden. Having to be nice about the French. And, worst of all, having to listen to Gracie Fields.

The Fifties

The most stressful thing about the 1950s, without a doubt, was having to listen to Alec Douglas-Home talking through that stupid slitty mouth. (GET SOME LIPS, FOR GOD'S SAKE!)

The Swinging Sixties

Again, Stress City. Imagine reading about the Summer of Love, the hippies, the drugs, the music, the sex, when you're a quality control manager living with your mother in Croydon.

The Moon Landing

People often say that the most stressful thing about the moon landing for the astronauts was coming back to Earth and finding their perspective on life had changed. I disagree. I think the most stressful thing about coming back from the moon must have been the jet lag. I mean, it's bad enough flying to Orlando. What must it be like when you've gone a quarter of a million miles? Poor old Neil Armstrong's probably still cooking himself a fried breakfast in the middle of the night.

What
Stress

What makes stress such a pressing problem today is that it is the most mundane things that cause the major stresses. Our homes, our families, our jobs, or simply moving around our high-speed, overcrowded towns and cities all create tensions which can build up and leave us suffering from a variety of stress-related symptoms. In this section of the book, I want to outline some of these elements of modern life and to identify what aspects of our lives we need to address if we are to deal with stress successfully.

Causes Today?

Stress at Home

Our homes should be the one place where we can relax and feel safe from the pressures of the world outside. Sadly, this is often not the case. Instead, our homes are hotbeds of tension and anxiety, and being at home can be as stress-inducing as trying to have fun in Switzerland. Moreover, it is not even what we do at home that causes this, but the actual fabric of the building itself, as the following illustrates.

Stress points in the home

Here are some pictures of a typical home (well, I say typical, but actually it's not – it's my home and mine isn't typical since most homes have doors on their hinges, coathangers that live in the wardrobe rather than everywhere else in the house, and a decor that, if not consistent throughout the house, doesn't mix Tuscan farmhouse with Texas Homecare). Opposite each picture is a list identifying the major stress points of each floor. You will also see the occasional black triangle. These represent areas so stressful that they should be avoided at all costs. If possible, you should also mentally blame the previous occupants of the house for having created them.

Basement

Kitchen

1. Under the washing-up bowl – Don't go here, unless you're a wildlife documentary-maker.

2. Cupboard under the sink – A variety of kitchen cleaners that you'll never ever use, such as Groutitout, an anti-mildew grout polish, and Zap! for the insides of 100% brass pipes. However, what you will never find here is something you can actually use to clean the kitchen.

3. Cupboards – Nothing usable here either. You'll come back at midnight, starving to death, and all you'll be able to rustle up is a garam masala, dried oregano and black peppercorn bake. If you're lucky, you'll find a couple of stray, very stale water biscuits that fell out of the packet and got trapped behind the oregano.

4. Grill – You don't dare take the foil off the grill pan. It's safer just to put more foil on each time you use it. The trouble is, no matter how much foil you put on it, everything ever cooked on the grill smells of fishfingers.

STRESSED ERIC

5. Table – This was once your pride and joy. Beautiful pine from Habitat, costing a fortune. Now dotted with scratches, burns and evidence that your eldest once tried to get off some candle wax with a Brillo pad. Try to avoid looking at it in daylight – it'll only make you cry.

6. Dresser – Have tried to achieve English Heritage Country Kitchen effect by displaying plates on dresser. In reality, have achieved Chipped Non-matching Crockery on Old Bureau That Won't Fit Anywhere Else in the House effect.

7. Fridge – Eight different pints of milk, all past their sell-by dates, two slices of processed cheese and a half-empty can of Special Brew. On the door there is children's art you felt compelled to attach even though it's crap.

8. Yucca plant – Dead.

29

Ground Floor

Living Room

1. Dining table – Never used. Who on earth would come to dinner with you?

2. Curtains – They don't quite meet in the middle. You either suffer permanent reminder of this or let the whole world see into your useless house.

3. Holes in wall – Abortive attempt at picture-hanging.

4. Horrific picture by 'local artist' – Was it really worth it?

5. Sofa – So worn you can see the outline of people's buttocks on the cushions.

6. Bay window – Huge cracks all round window. Reminder that you're suffering worse subsidence than Venice.

7. Floor – Began with rough boards, with apparent potential to be stripped and polished into exquisite wooden floor. Instead, sanded down to expose large expanses of hardboard with Tully & Sons, Erith (0181 774 2883) written all over it.

8. Weeping fig plant – Dead.

STRESSED ERIC

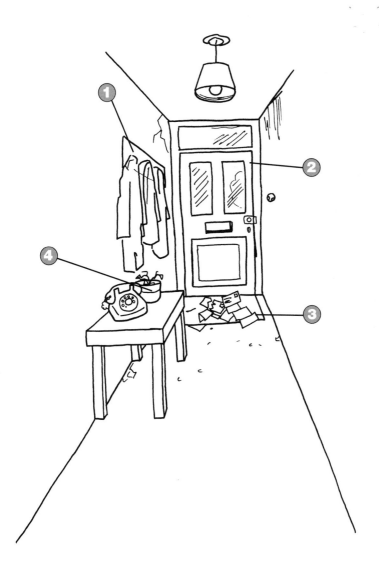

Hall

1. Coat rack – Inexplicable number of out-of-season coats that seem to belong to someone else.

2. Front door – Warped. Requires hefty shoulder charge to open. Tiny, impractical letter box.

3. Mat – Horribly mangled post.

4. African violet – Dying.

First Floor

a Au Pair's Bedroom
One of the most stressful areas in the house. A kind of black hole into which things go and never come out, including cutlery, plates, contents of drinks cabinet and various members of the Slade Green Satanists Society.

b Master Bedroom
1. Wall – Paper-thin divider between this and the au pair's room.

2. Even more horrific picture by 'local artist' – It's one of his early ones.

3. Futon – Bought on basis that it's more comfortable and relaxing than a mattress. This would only be true if you had a mattress made out of corrugated iron, and even then it's a close-run thing.

4. Spider Plant – Requesting a priest.

c Daughter's Bedroom
Pony pictures, pony books, pony duvet cover, pony wallpaper, complete collection of My Little Pony. Heartbreaking reminder that you'll never make her happy because you can't afford a pony.

d Son's Bedroom
Just don't touch anything.

e Bathroom
5. Door – Directly opposite loo. Lock doesn't work – door liable to drift open.

6. Floor – Doubles as a paddling pool.

7. Bath – Tidemarks dating back to the Boer War.

8. Soap – Tiny, tiny sliver, but it's all there is in the house.

9. Toilet roll – Only one final wisp left – the bit that's actually glued to the roll.

10. Shower – Choice of scalding or Arctic.

11. Maidenhair fern – Very ill.

STRESSED ERIC

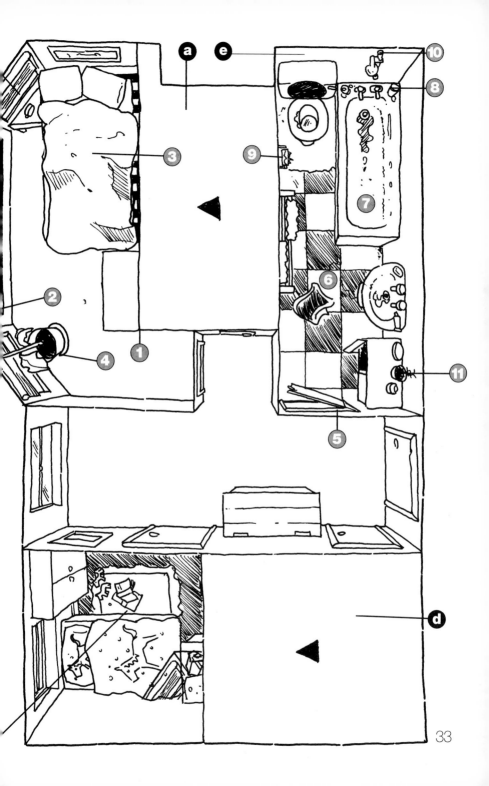

There seems to be a very simple solution to the problem of stress points in the home: eliminate them. And how do we do this? By getting the builders in.

Whoa, whoa, whoa.

Before you do this, you should remember that, in stress terms, having builders in rates just below having your kids abducted by aliens, who empty your bank account and impregnate your girlfriend on the way out. Perhaps the biggest problem of having builders in is that builders, like lawyers, are congenitally incapable of telling the truth. Here is a guide to translating what builders say:

Builder says: Estimate? £2000 all in, that's absolutely everything.
Builder means: Estimate? Upwards of £10,000 plus VAT.

Builder says: Yeah, there'll be a little bit of mess.
Builder means: It'll be like that scene in Lawrence of Arabia where they hit the really big sandstorm.

Builder says: It'll take three days tops.
Builder means: It'll take a minimum of a year.

Builder says: All it needs is a coat of varnish: there's nothing basically wrong with it.
Builder means: It's knackered, but we can cover that up for an extra fiver.

Builder says: If I were you, I'd have all that wiring out.
Builder means: I've just taken all that wiring out.

Builder says: No, don't worry about that crack, it's just the plaster.
Builder means: By the time the two halves of your house finally separate, I'll be retired and living in Marbella.

Builder says: Yeah, I can do that. I'm a plumber as well.
Builder means: I once unblocked my lavatory using a coat hanger.

Builder says: Let me just explain what's happened to your boiler.
Builder means: Prepare to spend the next hour in a state of almost total mental shutdown.

Builder says: Don't worry, I'll come back tomorrow and clear that up.
Builder means: Bye!

Sexual Stress

I've devoted a separate section to sex, since it is one of the most stressful human activities, even for an unstressed person. For a chronically stressed individual like myself it is the mother of all stresses, the Kilimanjaro of anxiety, the equivalent of a single-handed circumnavigation of the globe on a hostess trolley. So here is a list of the stressful incidents that can ruin sex:

- **The Mormons call.**

- **It takes you four hours and a team of people to put the condom on the right way round.**

- **The headboard breaks off mid-passion, concussing your partner.**

- **Even though you put the answerphone on, you suddenly hear your mother's voice saying, 'I know it's only Easter but have you decided what you're doing for Christmas yet?'**

- **Your partner stops for a moment to take some anti-depressants.**

- **You are ripping each other's clothes off when you remember you're wearing three-day-old X-Files underpants with the words 'The Truth Is In Here' on the front.**

- **You suddenly say something out of a porn film like, 'Come on now, baby, ride me home.'**

- **During foreplay, the only thing she says is, 'Ow'.**

- **You suddenly stop and realize you don't know what to do next.**

- **You discover she's more inexperienced than you thought when you ask her if she wants to go on top and she says, 'On top of what?'**

- **You notice traces of stubble on her chest.**

- **You suddenly become aware of your children filming you for a school project.**

Sex Diary

The main reason sex causes such huge levels of stress is that what one expects is very different from what one gets. Here is a comparison between the ideal and the stressful reality of what many people experience.

The Ideal Sexual Encounter		*The Stressed Sexual Encounter*
Superb candlelit meal cooked by self.	1	**Cook disastrous meal – the chicken is like pulp and the vegetables have been massacred to the point where if they were corpses you'd need dental records to identify them.**
You play superb smoochy music and do superb smoochy dancing with her.	2	**Desperately look for smoochy music, but kids have put LPs back in wrong sleeves. Find Barry White's Greatest Hits but inside is Russian Red Army Choir. Play it anyway.**
Having established an easy physical rapport, a sensuous massage lasting six and a half hours is the natural next step…	3	**Keep putting an arm behind her on sofa while conducting ludicrous monologue on the fact that the Russian Red Army Choir is in its own way just as sexy as Barry White, it's just less obvious.**
…followed by three and a half hours foreplay.	4	**Pounce.** **Fumble.** **She screams and leaves in a taxi.**
Multiple climaxes occur over the next few days.	5	**Masturbate furiously for the next few years using underwear section of Argos catalogue.**

Sexual Positions

Some of the key sexual positions that cause us so much stress. If possible try to avoid these:

The Please-Hurry-Up-I-Can't-Breathe position

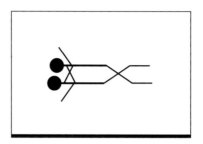

The Well-I'm-Sorry-But-They-Managed-It-Perfectly-Well-In-Basic-Instinct position

The I-Know-You-Think-This-Is-Degrading-To-Women-But-To-Be-Honest-It's-Part–Of-The-Fun position

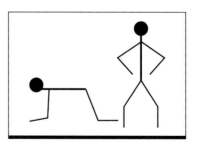

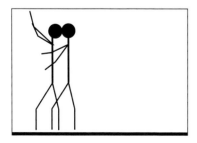

The This-Is-So-Unromantic-I-Know-But-We've-Only-Got-Five-Minutes-Before-The-Kids-Come-Back-From-School position

Stress at Work

The workplace is an extremely stressful environment where unhealthy air conditioning, cramped offices, temperamental computers and dodgy communications systems can all cause anxiety. However, what makes the workplace really stressful is the people we work with. Whether it's the batty old cleaning lady, the demanding boss, or the incompetent secretary, problematic human interactions in the office are the biggest single cause of stress in many people's lives.

My own personal experience certainly bears this out, particularly with reference to the phrase 'incompetent secretary'. Alison Scrapey has been working for me for many years, and she has consistently fallen short of what would be considered an acceptable standard. This has placed added stresses on me since I have often ended up doing her job as well as my own. It seems to me she is far too concerned with her social life, which has not only crept into her work life but, recently, seems to have driven through it in a Chieftain Tank. I finally confronted Alison last week upon discovery of the quarterly phone bill for my office, which, alarmingly, was bigger than that of the dealing room of an international bank. I asked Alison to explain what the calls were and to justify them. In doing so, I was hoping to use the mode of confrontation to reduce my stress levels. Unfortunately, as you'll see from the results she produced, my hopes were dashed and my stress levels increased to those of an astronaut on re-entry.

☎ Data Department Phone Bill

		0181 946 6028	7:58
	9:42	0171 636 1846	24:30
3 March	9:50	0181 946 6028	6:13
3 March	10:15	01962 457002	3:50
3 March	11:01	0171 636 1846	1:07:24
3 March	11:05	0121 236 5425	14:06
3 March	12:14	0181 946 6028	2:53:37
3 March	12:29	01962 457002	31:55
3 March	15:26	0171 920 9511	18:08
3 March	15:58	0181 946 6028	4:22
3 March	16:16	0171 636 1846	2:49
3 March	6:21	0181 293 4452	13:42
3 March	16:24	0121 449 2336	5:57
3 March	16:38		

International Calls

			001 333 4355990	14:23
		16:45	0034 900 624533	23:58
3 March	USA	17:00	10248 00 7104240	35:14
3 March	Malaga	17:24	001 333 4355990	44:03
3 March	Seychelles	18:00	00354 23 588	1:17:44
3 March	USA	18:45		
3 March	Iceland			

Alison's Explanation

'I had to phone Julie 'cause I'd heard she was slagging me off at Debbie's party, so I phoned her and I said, "What was you saying about me at Debbie's party 'cause I've heard you were slagging me off and I want to know what you said," and she said, "It weren't me, it was Shenella, she slagged you off," and I said, "She never, Shenella wouldn't slag me off," and Julie said, "Ask Debbie then, 'cause it was her party," so I phoned Debbie and said, "Julie says it was Shenella slagged me off at your party," and Debbie said, "She never," and I said, "Well, Julie said she did," and Debbie said, "If anyone slagged you off at my party I reckon it was Julie," so I had to phone Julie back and I said, "Debbie says it weren't Shenella, it was you," and Julie said, "It was Shenella, it's just that Debbie won't tell the truth about her 'cause they're cousins and Shenella bought her a porcelain spaniel for her wedding present," so I phoned Shenella and said, "Julie says you slagged me off at Debbie's party," and Shenella says, "I never, I wouldn't travel all the way from Winchester to just outside Croydon Airfield just to slag someone off unless it was Julie 'cause she's always been a right mouthy cow," so then I had to phone Debbie to tell her what Shenella had said about Julie and I said to her, "Shenella slagged Julie off and said she reckons she's a right mouthy cow," and then I remembered I had to phone me Mum who's gone up Birmingham to see the Ideal Bed Exhibition at the NEC and she's staying with Shenella's gran who lives in Solihull, and I told my Mum what Julie had said about Shenella slagging me off and how Debbie had said it was Julie, and me Mum said, "Well, what was it what was actually said when whoever it was slagged you off slagged you off?" So I rang Julie and asked her and she said, "Ask Shenella, she should know," and I phoned Shenella and she said, "Phone Wendy, the fat one with a perm who works with Debbie, 'cause she heard what was said," so I phoned Wendy and she said it was actually Debbie who'd slagged me off, so I phoned Julie and said, "That Wendy reckons it was Debbie who slagged me off," and Julie says, "You should confront Debbie and ask her," so I rang Debbie and asked her and she said, "All right I'll tell you what I said," and I said, "SHUT YOUR MOUTH, YOU COW, I'M NOT INTERESTED." Then I had to phone Dean Tothill, my boyfriend, and tell him what had happened and he said he didn't care, so I packed him in and then I was bawling me eyes out 'cause I'd packed him in and I rang me Mum up Shenella's gran to tell her, and then I had to phone everyone else to tell them, so I rang Barbara in Washington DC and Charmaine who's on holiday in Malaga and Zoe who's modelling turtleshell bikinis in the Seychelles and Barbara in Washington again and then Sigurd in Iceland, who's this bloke I met up Friday Nite Fever in Eltham last summer. Then I went home at eight o'clock at night so that's three hours overtime you owe me.'

Children and Stress

In stress terms, bringing up children is one of the most taxing things a human can ever do. In ancient myth, Sisyphus was forced to roll a huge, heavy boulder up a steep mountain every day. On reaching the top, the boulder would fall to the bottom and he would have to repeat the task. This went on every day for eternity. This is like being a parent, except, of course, Sisyphus was the lucky one – think how much more irritating it would have been with two kids demanding to be read a story at the same time.

The five most stressful things about being a parent are:

1. The only edition of *Match of the Day* you're awake for is the early one on Sunday morning.

2. Having to boast about your child when he's self-evidently talentless and ugly.

3. Being given Fleetwood Mac CDs for Christmas because people think 'you're that sort of age'.

4. Having to sing 'Horsey, horsey, don't you stop' and do the actions while driving all the way from London to St Ives.

5. Hearing yourself initiate a Play-Doh versus Plasticine debate at a dinner party.

Of course, you love your children for what they are. The problem arises when what they are is a disappointment. Sometimes you cannot help but compare your children to their peers, for example, the prissy madam next door. No matter how often people say comparisons are invidious and that everyone develops at their own rate, this is of little comfort if your child seems to be developing at the rate of a new Ice Age.

Compare these two school reports. Which parent do you think is likely to experience the greater stress?

THE HEATH SCHOOL

Pupil's Report: Autumn Term 1997

NAME: **Heather Perfect**

CLASS: **4**

Writing   Quite simply outstanding. Her script is superb and her vocabulary is extraordinary in one so young. Asked to write on the subject of 'My Holiday', Heather produced a consummate account of life on a big game reserve in Kenya, which displayed narrative tension, near-perfect structure and a sensitivity that would be rare in someone twice her age (I particularly enjoyed the chiselled beauty of the Masai people).

Reading

Quite simply outstanding. For me, the highlight of the term was to glance up during the coach trip to Chessington Zoo and see Heather clutching a copy of Madame Bovary.

Maths   Quite simply outstanding. In the end of term mental arithmetic quiz she not only calculated pi to 26 decimal places (I asked for two), she also squared it, cubed it and still had time to tidy up the maths cupboard.

Music and Movement   QUITE SIMPLY OUTSTANDING. HER DRAMATIC AND DANCE SKILLS SHONE THROUGH IN THE SCHOOL NATIVITY PLAY, AND AS FAR AS NEXT TERM'S SCHOOL CONCERT IS CONCERNED, I DON'T KNOW WHICH I'M LOOKING FORWARD TO MOST: THE BEETHOVEN SONATA OR THE MEDLEY FROM FUNNY GIRL!

Games and PE   QUITE SIMPLY OUTSTANDING. THIS TERM SHE HAS BROKEN THE UNDER-12S COUNTY RECORDS IN 100 METRES, 200 METRES, HURDLES, LONG JUMP, HIGH JUMP AND CROSS COUNTRY. SADLY, SHE FAILED TO BREAK THE POINTS-SCORING RECORD FOR GUARD IN NETBALL, SO HER EXISTING RECORD WILL HAVE TO STAND FOR ANOTHER YEAR!

THE HEATH SCHOOL
Pupil's Report: Autumn Term 1997

NAME: *Brian Feeble*

CLASS: *4*

Writing

Another disappointing term. His script is illegible and his control of vocabulary somewhat erratic. His essay, 'My Holiday', consisted entirely of one syllable words and the substance of the narrative — 'We were in the car. I was in the car. Dad was in the car. Claire was in the car' — led us to believe that no one ever left the car.

Reading

Another disappointing term. Brian still seems to derive abnormal pleasure from the Janet and John series, and while they are not completely without merit, his re-reading them for the fifth time is rather worrying.

Maths

Another disappointing term. Brian struggles with maths. He seems unable to grasp that 7×8 is always 56 regardless of context, time of day and his opinion.

Music and Movement

ANOTHER DISAPPOINTING TERM.
HE IS NEITHER MUSICAL NOR MOVES.

Games and PE

ANOTHER DISAPPOINTING TERM. IT IS A MEASURE OF HIS LACK OF PROGRESS THAT IN THE LONG JUMP HE STILL FAILS TO REACH THE SAND PIT, EVEN THOUGH ON THREE OCCASIONS WE'VE MOVED THE TAKE-OFF BOARD CLOSER. IN RUGBY, HE PERSISTS IN TACKLING HIS OWN TEAM MATES, AND ON ONE OCCASION MRS GILKES, WHO WAS OUT COLLECTING LEAVES FOR THE NATURE TABLE.

One of the most stressful things about being a parent is that children are forever falling ill, having accidents, or, in the case of my own daughter, Claire, developing alarming allergies to almost every object in the world. This not only provokes a lot of worry about their health but also launches you into the grisly and highly stressful world of hospitals, medicine and the risk of contagion.

Here is a good example of the kind of stress that I have to deal with. On Claire's birthday I bought her her first Walkman, naïvely expecting that the rest of the day would be filled with laughter, happiness and that slightly irritating noise that comes out of people's earphones. I was to be quickly disabused of this notion when she bounded into the bedroom and I gave her the present, wrapped in non-allergic wrapping paper with sterile ribbon. Her little face lit up as she inserted a cassette and put on the earphones. It was then that she started to scream. Here is an official record of the remainder of the day:

THE NEWTON HOSPITAL TRUST
M E D I C A L   C A R D

Name	CLAiRE FEEBLE			Sheet no: 1402
Admitted	**Time**	**Symptoms**	**Diagnosis**	**Recommended Treatment**
1/2/98	8.00am	Chronic swelling of ears	Suspected allergy to plastic/metal alloy material used to make Walkmans	Phenoglomin
1/2/98	8.10am	Chronic swelling of lips, mouth and tongue	Suspected allergy to Phenoglomin	Xiapathan
1/2/98	8.25am	Chronic swelling of entire head	Suspected allergy to Xiapathan	Just avoid Walkmans

Travelling and Stress

In the past, people tended to live their whole lives without ever travelling far. Today, in contrast, we spend much of our lives rushing further and further afield, ever faster, ever more frenetic. In this section, I have explored some of the chief ways in which travelling and modern transportation induce stress.

Driving

Cars are the most common form of transport and the most all-round stress-inducing, whether you are a complete beginner or an experienced motorist.

*Five stressful things that can occur
during your driving test*

1. You cause a pile-up before you've left the test centre.

2. By the end of the test, you have a family from Southend clinging to the bonnet.

3. There is a sudden bang, a yelp and part of an animal drops through the sunroof.

4. You accidentally switch on the radio and hear that the police are hunting you in connection with a series of motoring offences.

5. Your examiner turns out to be an obsessive Shakin' Stevens fan and sings 'Green Door' throughout the whole test.

But, of course, the stresses of driving begin before you've even put the key in the ignition. Like the family home, the family car is littered with stress points. Here is a diagram identifying the most crucial of these:

STRESSED ERIC

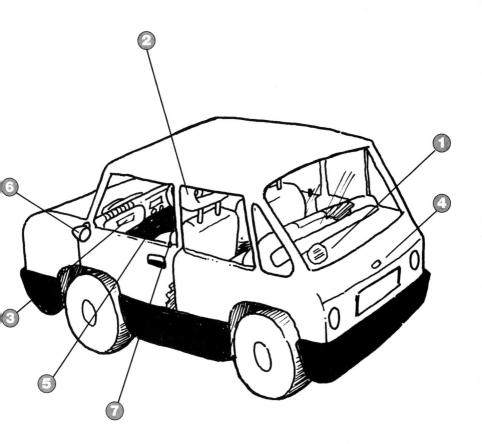

1. Sticker – you're now ashamed of this and have tried to peel it off, but the words 'My other car is a penis' are still visible.

2. Badly designed headrest – suitable only for basketball players.

3. Glove compartment – gloves never to be found here, nor useful book telling you how car works. However, should you need some horrible boiled sweets, a used tissue or a cassette of 'Smash Hits 1975' (why have you heard of only one of the tracks?), this is the place.

4. Boot – containing blanket and mysterious power tool (how did it get there?).

5. Smell of child's sick from four years ago.

6. The you-can-never-get-it-at-quite-the-right-angle wing mirror.

7. Childproof lock – opens only at high speed on motorway.

A Stressed Person's Guide to the Highway Code

If you read the Highway Code, you'll read about a world where roads are safe, motorists are sensible and courteous, and there are never more than four cars on a motorway at any given moment. On no account should you allow yourself to be lulled into a false sense of security by this particularly mendacious and misleading document. The following is intended as a corrective to such nonsensical propaganda and represents the horribly stressful reality of being a driver.

Traffic lights

Red means stop – unless you're going at seventy and you're late for your daughter's recorder concert, in which case it just means 'Whoops'.

Amber also means stop – unless you're going at seventy and you're late for your daughter's recorder concert, in which case it means 'Just this once, sonny'.

Green means go if the way is clear. In reality, it also means go if it isn't, especially if you're going at seventy and you're late for your daughter's recorder concert. (However, you should be prepared to swerve a lot and possibly confront a gaggle of other drivers all carrying baseball bats.)

STRESSED ERIC

Using the road

Here is a diagram of the layout of a typical inner city road. The carriageway is divided up to allow everyone to have sufficient room to move.

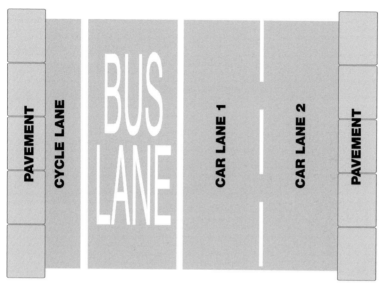

Or at least that's the theory. We all know that in practice the reality is much more stressful.

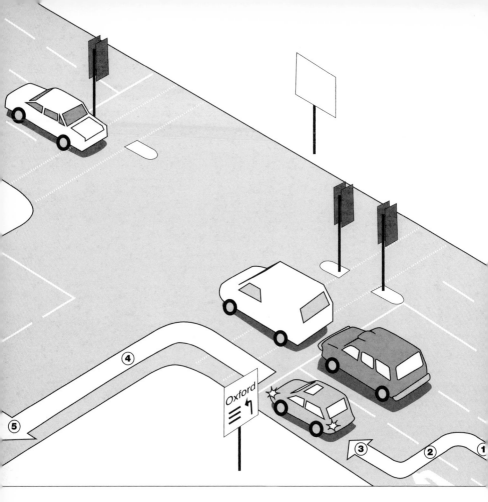

Lane Discipline

A normal driver's guide to getting in the right lane

1. Check road sign to see which lane you need for Oxford town centre.

2. Check position of other traffic and indicate.

3. Move into appropriate lane when it is safe to do so.

4. Once manoeuvre is safely completed, turn off indicator.

5. You arrive safely in Oxford town centre.

A stressed driver's guide to getting in the right lane

1. Can't see road sign for Oxford town centre.
   Guess which lane you want.

2. Lurch into it without looking. Exchange V-sign with taxi driver.

3. Realize you are in wrong lane. Lurch back again, nearly up-ending
   minibus full of primary school children.

4. Notice road sign. You were in the right lane. Try and get back in again.
   Cab driver blocks you off and calls you a dozy wanker.

5. You are forced to remain in this lane. Drive to Birmingham, then drive
   back and try again.

Road Signs

Road signs are stressful because they are largely irrelevant. They warn us about stupid things we don't need to be warned about. Take this sign:

This means wild animals. Well, I've never seen any wild animals and I've seen this sign hundreds of times. What we need is a whole new set of signs giving us useful and relevant information about the things we need to be warned about when driving. Here are some examples of road signs that would provide relevant and pertinent information for the stressed driver.

Beware – Reading is coming up

Terrible programme on Radio 4 approaching

Beware – awful rustic smell

Tedious scenery for the next 40 miles

Ugly hitchhikers ahead

Dull conversation in car for next 20 miles

STRESSED ERIC

Finally, here are some reminders which will help make driving less stressful.

1. Drive slowly near schools. Except when you're passing one of those terrifying south London comprehensives, in which case, drive like the wind.

2. Give way to buses whenever you can. Except when it's all about pride, in which case you should battle the bastard all the way up the High Street.

3. Always check there isn't a cyclist approaching when you open your driver's door. Failing that, follow the old musician's adage that if you're going to make a mistake, make a loud one and thrust the door open violently, sending him thumping into another dimension. This will render him completely unconscious, he won't remember a thing and you're in the clear.

4. Do not overtake unless you can do so safely. Except when you're stuck behind a tractor on the A11, in which case it's worth the risk.

5. Wherever possible, pull off the road into an area provided specifically for parking. Since there are currently only three of these available in Britain, use someone's drive instead and if you're caught, claim that your wife's having a baby.

Are you Stressed?

Given that you are likely to have a home, or a family, or a job, or a car, or maybe all of them, it is probable that you too will experience some stress in your life. It may be that certain physical difficulties you have are not the problems you think, but are actually stress-induced. To help you identify whether this is the case, here is some information about the symptoms of stress.

Symptoms of Stress

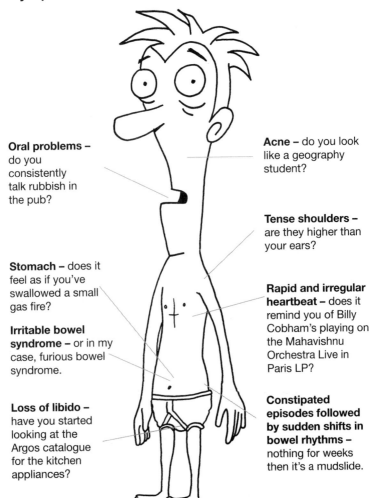

Oral problems – do you consistently talk rubbish in the pub?

Stomach – does it feel as if you've swallowed a small gas fire?

Irritable bowel syndrome – or in my case, furious bowel syndrome.

Loss of libido – have you started looking at the Argos catalogue for the kitchen appliances?

Acne – do you look like a geography student?

Tense shoulders – are they higher than your ears?

Rapid and irregular heartbeat – does it remind you of Billy Cobham's playing on the Mahavishnu Orchestra Live in Paris LP?

Constipated episodes followed by sudden shifts in bowel rhythms – nothing for weeks then it's a mudslide.

STRESSED ERIC

Writing a Stress Chart

You can also evaluate your stress levels by drawing up a simple stress chart and measuring how you react to different events and experiences. List various things that have caused you some anxiety and measure their impact out of a maximum stress score of 100. Here are two contrasting stress charts:

A Normal Person's Stress Chart

Bereavement 100
Divorce..98
Being fired 97
Moving house...97
Financial difficulties 94
Child excluded from school...................................85
Bad weather on holiday 46
Traffic jam on way to work 41

A Stressed Person's Stress Chart

Bereavement..100
Being fired 100
Bad weather on holiday 100
Getting the cellophane off a new videotape 100
Having to listen to bagpipes...............................100
Having to spend more than half an hour in Reading....100
Trying to open a bag of in-flight peanuts 100

In the end, the easiest way of diagnosing stress is simply to think about your typical day and to assess whether it exhibits well-balanced and calm tendencies, or whether there are signs that you may need some help in relaxing and coping with what life throws at you. Another useful exercise is to make a pie chart, divide it into 24 hours and see what proportion of each day is taken up with stress-provoking activities. Here are some examples of a healthy model and an unhealthy one.

A Healthy Day

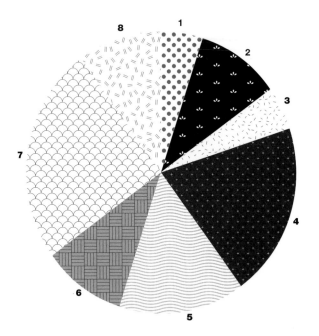

1. **Spend hour running in park in healthy quest for fitness (5%)**

2. **Dynamically chair high-powered meeting at work (10%)**

3. **Lunchtime recital at Wigmore Hall by brilliant young pianist: Brahms, Haydn and Chopin (5%)**

4. **Bond with your children, increasing the sense of togetherness and family (15%)**

5. **Throw a successful dinner party and laugh in the company of close friends (20%)**

6. **Enjoy mutually fulfilling sex with your devoted long-term partner (15%)**

7. **Sleep peacefully (20%)**

8. **Wonderful dreams of former school beauty queen who's now your wife (10%)**

STRESSED
ERIC

An Unhealthy Day

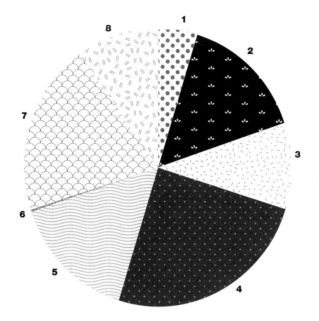

1. Spend hour running up and down stairs in panic quest for keys (5%)

2. Go to wrong meeting because secretary has misinformed you. Arrive at right meeting as it ends to find out it was a huge success because you weren't there (15%)

3. Busker outside office still playing wrong chords to 'Streets of London' (10%)

4. Bickering with your children, increasing the likelihood of later visits to family therapist (25%)

5. Get drunk at someone else's dinner party and bore someone you barely know about how much better life was when you were a student (20%)

6. Three minutes with the Argos catalogue (0.0000000001%)

7. Lie awake until you drop off to sleep five minutes before it's time to get up (15%)

8. Nightmare of former school bully now stalking you in adult life (10%)

Let's

Deal with Stress

Having explored things that cause stress and the terrible physical and mental toll they take on us, it's now time to look at how we can combat them. In this section, I'll examine numerous approaches to stress management, some familiar, some less familiar, but all of them put forward by various experts and authorities as valid and helpful ways of countering the misery of stress. I have tried all the therapies I list below, and you will see that I am not always 100% convinced of their validity. Nonetheless, you may find them more useful than I – that is your prerogative.

A Question **of Perspective**

One of the most terrible things about being stressed is that you lose any sense of perspective. It feels as if you are the only person in the world who is tense, while everybody around you looks calm, confident and relaxed. You must remember that this is nonsense. On the outside they may look like Desmond Lynam, but on the inside they're like the woman with the quivering voice in Coronation Street who worries about everything. I decided to prove to myself that I'm not the only stressed person in the world by talking to my neighbours. As well as making me feel less isolated, I thought this might give me valuable insights into how others deal with tension.

Mrs Perfect seems to lead a charmed and stress-free life. But what, I wondered, would I find beneath the veneer? I wrote to her asking about her experience of stress. A couple of days later I received this reply:

STRESSED
ERIC

La Maison des Parfaits

15 PARK ROAD, LONDON SE2O

Dear Eric

I'm sorry not to have responded sooner, but we've been terribly busy what with Heather's recital, the opening of Jean Paul's new restaurant in Mayfair, and the dinner party to celebrate the sale of the millionth copy of Ray's book *Health, Wealth and Happiness* (Splendid Books, £25.99).

In answer to your question, yes, I certainly do feel stress. Coordinating all the facets of a large dinner party, for instance – even if you do have the help of award-winning au pairs, outside caterers and professional table decorators – is a remarkably taxing business. One has such issues to attend to. The seating plan alone would reduce a lesser person to tears. If one invites an MP from one party, is one duty bound to invite one from the opposition as well? Is it safe to seat a controversial BAFTA winner next to a captain of industry? And just where do you put a deposed African president?

So you see I do feel stress. Of course, I wouldn't be so patronising as to suggest that my stresses are anything compared to yours, you poor dear man, having to cope with your backward, sickly children, and that criminally inclined au pair. No, I realise only too well that I've been lucky. Perhaps the heady mix of genes inherited from an Olympic decathlete father and a quantum physicist mother must somehow have helped me struggle through, perhaps on reflection a more potent inheritance than you were bequeathed by dear darling Joan and poor doddery Derek. That, alas, is the lottery of life, and it has obviously been my lucky lot to have proven a double rollover winner every month since I was born.

I do hope the book goes well. How brave of you to become a first-time author with only two and a half weeks before publication, and in such a saturated market!

À bientôt

Madame Parfait

Exercise and Sport

A good physical workout is supposedly one of the best ways to reduce stress. Many experts maintain that any kind of exercise or sporting activity is beneficial not only physically, but also in dealing with the pressures of modern living. However, this is clearly nonsense. Unless one is very careful, exercise or sporting activity will actually increase your stress level either through physical discomfort and injury or straightforward social embarrassment. So here is a guide to various sports and games and why you should probably avoid them all.

Rugby

Rugby is the most stressful sport you can get involved in. The only object in rugby is for large men to try and hurt you as much as they can over 80 minutes. If you survive the game on the pitch, you've still got to survive the clubhouse afterwards, where grown men light each other's farts and do unspeakable things with Tizer bottles. If you don't join in, they'll probably leave you naked and covered in hair remover in a field near Reading. Suicide is preferable.

Swimming

At the local swimming pool, hazards include:

- **screaming kamikaze teenagers diving on to your head**

- **lumpy middle-aged women doing very slow breaststroke**

- **a very cocky and very hairy Greek man who knows he's the only person in town who can do the butterfly**

- **swallowing a mouthful of water and then hearing a mother say to her fretful three year old, 'Of course it doesn't matter, everyone wees in the pool'.**

You start off thinking you'll do four lengths of breaststroke, four lengths of crawl and four of backstroke, but then you do half a width of interrupted doggie paddle, give up in disgust and return to the changing room to find your wallet's been nicked. Four years later you still smell of chlorine.

STRESSED
ERIC

Football

This is probably one of the less harmful sports, unless you get involved in a game against a pub team called The Vicious Squaddie from Hackney, in which case, it could lead to serious injury or even death. Try to avoid, also, games involving teams of 'fathers'. These are a bad idea because all the players will not only be unfit, they will also be married and 40 and will have suffered almost total sexual frustration for a number of years. Hence, their homicidal desire to take it out on the opposition team. A game against them could make you long for more fixtures with The Vicious Squaddie.

Stressed Forty-something's Football Kit

Shirt – bought in the early 1980s to replace the unfashionable shirt from the 1970s, which is now fashionable again, unlike the shirt from the 1980s

Ball – always slightly under-inflated and therefore stings on contact. In wet weather the imprint of the manufacturer comes off on your forehead

Shorts – from the early 1970s, very tight, showing top of chicken leg, pronounced policeman's bottom and yet, disappointingly, virtually no evidence of the sexual organs (especially on a cold day)

Boots – uncleaned since 1974. Your feet still smell from them hours after you've put your shoes back on

61

Martial Arts

There are two kinds of martial art. On the one hand there's Tai Chi. This is a non-violent martial art, which immediately makes it silly. Let's face it, if you don't smash a few bricks, it's not a proper martial art, is it? A non-contact martial art simply doesn't make sense. It's like full-contact chess. Ignore.

Karate, on the other hand, is incredibly macho, but in its own way it's just as silly as Tai Chi. If God had meant us to break bricks with our foreheads, he wouldn't have created pickaxes. Apparently, with training, it doesn't hurt. I don't believe that. Maybe it doesn't hurt as much as it would have done if you hadn't done any training, but we're talking marginal here. Surely it's like the difference between jumping off the 70th floor of a hotel and landing on your head and jumping off the 71st.

Water Sports

Weil's disease, hypothermia, cholera, dysentery, hepatitis B, being hit by a passing speedboat, unexpected changes in currents causing death by drowning. Need I say more?

Shooting

Cathartic, a release, a way of de-stressing through the safe application of violence. The only trouble is, you're not allowed to shoot the things you really want to – like the people next door.

Golf

Into the great outdoors. Long walks in gorgeous weather through beautifully sculpted courses. Freedom, enjoyment, absorption. But, oh how fantastically annoying trying to get that stupid little ball in that stupid little hole. It won't go in, will it? It goes left, it goes right, it goes nowhere. There's no pattern to it at all. Golf is the devil's game. Who else could have invented a sport in which the most minute things make the biggest differences? Where, if you move your little finger a millimetre on the club handle, the ball ends up in Australia? Forget it.

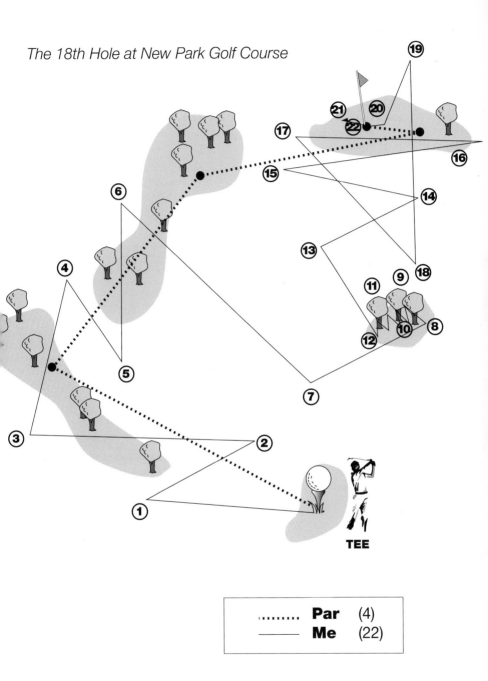

The 18th Hole at New Park Golf Course

TEE

	Par	(4)
·········	**Par**	(4)
——	**Me**	(22)

Cricket

Cricket could be relaxing, especially if you are fielding on the boundary and it's a lovely day. That is, of course, unless you're playing on a council-owned public pitch in London, where there's liable to be another pitch next to yours and you could easily get hit in the back of the head by someone else's ball. This highlights the only real drawback of cricket: the ball, a horrible hard object which you should try to avoid at all costs.

Three practical ways to avoid the ball in cricket:

1. **Volunteer to make the tea. Everyone takes tea so seriously in cricket that they will instantly forgive this obvious act of cowardice on your part.**
2. **Volunteer to drive the bloke who's just got hit on the back of the head to hospital.**
3. **Be on holiday while the game is on.**

Skating

Looks fun, graceful and smooth on the telly. In reality, it means frequently falling on to a surface harder than concrete every 20 seconds for an hour, and being immediately crushed by the dozen people who are skating behind you. You could get the same effect if you threw yourself onto your patio at home and got someone else to drop a sofa on you. You'd also definitely avoid catching athlete's foot off the bloke who used your skates before you.

STRESSED ERIC

Cards

In some ways it sounds ideal. It is mentally engrossing, physically non-stressful, but you do have to look the part. You've got to be smooth, you've got to be cool; above all you've got to be slick. You really shouldn't play cards if it's going to take you an hour to re-align the edges once you've shuffled the pack. And if you find that dealing cards out always takes longer than playing the hand (as it does in my case) then you should look at a different sport altogether. Some card games you should consider more than others. Snap is easy but stressfully repetitive and leads to bickering. On the other hand it doesn't cost you your house as poker can. Bridge is far too complicated, whilst it is okay if you want to spend a whole evening with a bunch of very old ladies from a rest home in Eastbourne. Then there's the game that people play on their own when they lay all the cards down in piles – I mean, what's the point of that?

Overall then, if you're the Cincinatti Kid, cards is a good idea. If you are a clumsy oaf like me who can't win milk bottle tops off his friends then read the paper instead. (Although this is stressful itself. See section entitled "Trying to turn the page of a broadsheet newspaper on the Northern Line").

Badminton

Should be the perfect unstressed sport because it's easy. The trouble is it's so easy it's completely naff. Let's face it, badminton is a weed's version of tennis. The 'ball' floats ludicrously, allowing a 95 year old with a zimmer frame time to get underneath it. The rackets are puny. The sound the shuttlecock makes on impact is a ludicrous sort of 'thwimp'. Even the people who play it are naff – firms of chartered surveyors and members of Methodist youth clubs. (It's a bit of a give-away that the only other game they play is table tennis.) Add in the fact that badminton gear is totally uncool (too much white and far too tight) and you should give the game a complete miss.

Exercising in the Home

Given the high stress levels associated with any sport or game undertaken outside the home, many people find it more therapeutic to exercise in their own space. Many manuals are available which offer regimes of exercises to do at home to help reduce tension. These are, however, typically over-demanding and written by people who have no conception of what it's like to be a forty-year-old divorcee with the suppleness of pre-stressed concrete.

Here is a course of exercises from a book called *For Bod's Sake!* which I have amended to better reflect the realities of what can be achieved.

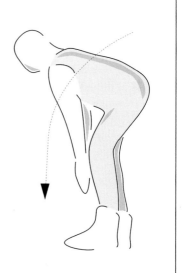

What the manual says
Touch your toes half a dozen times, then hold the bent position for 30 seconds.

What you should be satisfied with
Lunge downwards three times. Be content if you manage to flick the top part of your shin with your fingertips. Then slump backwards on to the sofa breathing heavily.

STRESSED ERIC

What the manual says

Sit cross-legged on the floor, putting
your palms down flat either side of you.
Inhale deeply and hold your breath for
20 seconds. Then exhale over a
similar period.

What you should be satisfied with

**Try to stuff one leg under the other
as best you can (you probably
haven't sat cross-legged since
school and one leg will probably
go, not the other). Start to keel
over backwards. Don't resist. Lie
spark out on the floor, feeling
pleased with yourself that you
haven't split anything.**

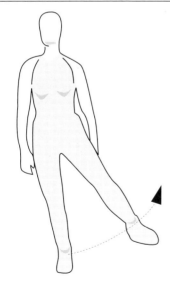

What the manual says

Stand on one leg with the other raised at
an angle of 30 degrees and the toe
pointed down to the floor. Slowly rotate
both arms in large, free-swinging circles,
for 20 minutes, breathing deeply.

What you should be satisfied with

**Stand on one leg. Feel startling pain
around the kneecap. Manage a
couple of furious windmills with
your arms before giving up and
spending afternoon in an armchair
watching the racing.**

The Wisdom of the East (or not)

In recent years, many have rejected traditional Western ways of dealing with stress and have turned instead to ideas and techniques from ancient Eastern civilizations. Various forms of massage, mysticism and other holistic approaches are becoming increasingly popular, so I thought it essential to experiment with some of these. Here are the results of my researches.

Why Reflexology Is Not For Me

Reflexology is the art of massaging the foot to increase bodily well-being. Each part of the foot corresponds to a part of the body and the theory maintains that to relax that part of the foot is to heal and strengthen the corresponding body part. On the surface, this seems perfect. It is ideal for people like me, who are uneasy about taking off their clothes for a body massage. It also has the added advantage that unnerving bodily contact is confined to a part of the anatomy you probably don't mind your mother touching. However, when I went to see a reflexologist, I encountered a problem far more insurmountable than mere modesty; namely, the sheer sensitivity of my feet. No sooner did the reflexologist put his fingers on my soles than I was giggling like a loon and writhing around as if going into spasm. The more he tried, the worse it became, until he finally lost patience and grabbed hold of my foot with both hands. By this point I was in complete hysterics and totally unable to control myself. I involuntarily kicked him in the head, sending him toppling unconscious into a tub of talcum powder, at which point I left discreetly.

As with so many of these therapies, books and manuals on reflexology do not seem to have much grasp of reality. To redress the balance, here is a diagram showing what reflexologists think a foot is like. Next to it is a diagram showing what my foot is actually like.

STRESSED
ERIC

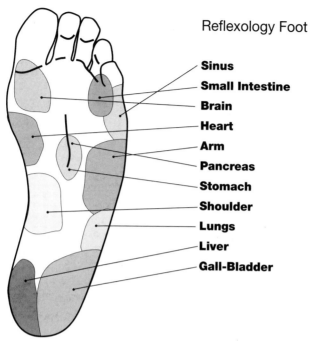

Reflexology Foot

- Sinus
- Small Intestine
- Brain
- Heart
- Arm
- Pancreas
- Stomach
- Shoulder
- Lungs
- Liver
- Gall-Bladder

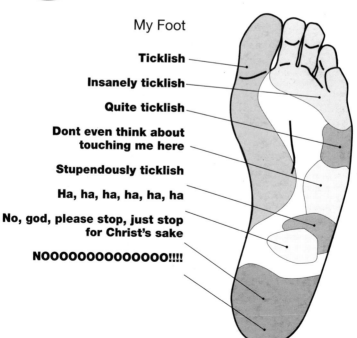

My Foot

- Ticklish
- Insanely ticklish
- Quite ticklish
- Dont even think about touching me here
- Stupendously ticklish
- Ha, ha, ha, ha, ha, ha
- No, god, please stop, just stop for Christ's sake
- NOOOOOOOOOOOOOO!!!!

Feng Shui

This is the ancient Chinese art of arranging the interior of your house so that the energies of everything in it are in harmony. Furniture and possessions are aligned to create a single unity. Feng Shui, of course, presupposes that such a thing exists in the first place. I would dispute that. In the case of my living room, I think there is a very obvious limit to the amount of harmony you can get out of one old red sofa, a knackered wicker chair with an orange cushion that clashes with the sofa, and a bookcase that looks terrible wherever you put it. It would tax an army of Feng Shui masters to create something out of that lot. Ditto my bathroom, with its random tattered décor caused by half a dozen missing tiles which I've never got round to replacing. As for the airing cupboard, I don't know about creating harmony within – I'd be happy if I could just find someone able to open the door without the entire contents falling out.

In fact, I reckon that my entire house is a challenge to the idea that there is any single guiding force operating in the world other than bad planning allied to total lack of money. Besides, let's be realistic about this. Feng Shui was devised by a lot of wizened old Chinese codgers who probably lived in monasteries and had no possessions. They certainly didn't have to contend with 12,000-piece Lego kits, eight changes of clothing for Barbie and an au pair who seems to buy knickers less for wearing than for leaving in the living room. And anyway, why on earth should we take any notice of something some old buffer in Beijing thought 3000 years ago? What would happen if we started borrowing from them wholesale? How about binding your wife's feet so they take on the erotic form of the lotus blossom? Is that a good idea? And what about burying people, digging them up a few days later and then burying them again? Mmm, that sounds fantastic. Let's adopt that.

It's also often forgotten that the theory of Feng Shui rests on the assumption that there are dragons asleep in the ground under each building and they must not be disturbed. I can tell you for a fact that there is no dragon asleep under my house. I know exactly what is under my house – a Victorian molasses factory. In summer you can smell it through the kitchen floor.

In fact, like so many other pseudo-scientific modern fads nicked unthinkingly from periods in history when they'd just as soon shove pokers up your bum as give you directions, the whole idea of Feng Shui, rather than reducing stress, brings me out in a furious rage.

STRESSED ERIC

DIY Dry Shiatsu Massage for the Face

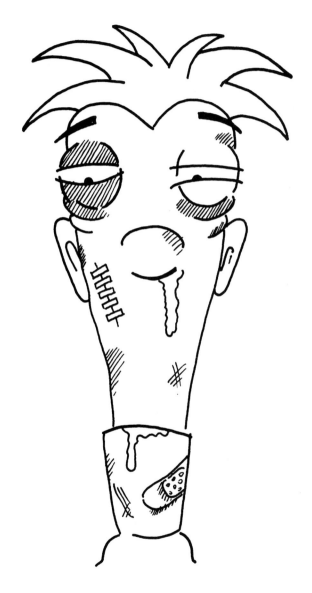

Why do-it-yourself dry shiatsu massage is not the answer.

Massage

Massage is becoming increasingly popular as a way of ridding the body of stress. Rather than writing this section myself (and given that the library suddenly decided to invent its own bank holiday on the day I was researching this bit), I have asked my ex-wife Liz to provide a brief introduction to some new forms of massage. She is adamant that these are affirmative, life enhancing and therapeutic practices which have enriched her soul and given her inner peace. I, on the other hand, feel that they are a lot of expensive tosh. I leave you to judge.

The Art of Bawandic Foot Massage
by Umgala T'Puupuu (formerly Liz Feeble)

I am thankful for being able to share with you some of the essential spiritual and physiotemporal energies which flow from an ancient teaching known as Gwb (or Bawandic foot massage). To perform the exercises below is not merely to replenish body and mind, but also to allow the true self to grow and empty the soul of all negativity, all animosity and all bitterness (although it's probably likely that my bastard charlatan of an ex-husband will edit this bit out).

Many thanks to the beloved who have nurtured me throughout this project. To my Caleb, strong, sure, a rock, patient when I needed him to be, and courageous (particularly when I slipped during Famula Gazooba and he had to put his own shoulder back); to Brian Robertson for his sensitive and loving illustrations done using his own excrement (why can't more artists be self-sufficient like this?); to the people of northeastern Brazil – may your time not be slow in coming and may the seeds of Imwa implant themselves in Gemini. Finally, love the trees, be with the flowers, hug the Earth. No person can destroy what one person's destruction destroys in another person's destruction. The translations have been provided by Hampstead Friends of the Third World. The fight goes on. Umzabwa.

STRESSED
ERIC

1 Famulu gazooba fadumbwe quimzabo.

(trans. Together we the grapes of life tread in, flames, ears, mud, regret all in the soup we call life ready to eat, mmmm, delicious.)

② Yo yo puba in dobe wahula

(trans. Yes, yes, taste my balls, yes,
okay, like the soup also delicious.)

(3) Waab in galoop a semme olookenz abili sum gulap umm popo imcilli selombwe.

(trans. To prise gently the earliest spring flower is nothing compared to the enjoyment joyfully of striking the young son of the head of the tribe, who himself would strike were the maidens of the village not witnessing the birth of another of their kind some weeks early and quite small, so let soup be prepared in honour and celebration, a soup that even the struck man can enjoy through the side of his mouth.)

A World of Stress

People often maintain that an answer to stress is to have a holiday and leave behind all those things that create stressful situations. What they overlook is that travelling abroad brings you into contact with a whole new set of stresses that are worse than the ones you left behind. So to help you decide whether trips abroad are worth the hassle, here is a lay person's stress guide to travel abroad, listing the pros and cons of the most popular holiday destinations.

Italy

For:	Against:
Great food, great drink, great weather	Great big trouble if anything goes wrong.
	There are four types of police and none of them are interested. You've got more chance of getting the Pope to come round than you have of getting a plumber. And if you become ill, you've got more chance of getting a plumber than you have of getting an ambulance.

Sweden

For:	Against:
Stockholm is one of the most beautiful cities in the world. It has art galleries, theatres, huge palaces.	It's so expensive you can't afford to visit any of them. You can't afford to eat, you can't afford to drink, you can't afford to do anything but sit in your B&B all day and cry. (You'll have to use your hands to dry your eyes – tissues are £10 for a packet of five.)

Bulgaria

For:	Against:
People say 'Oooh, it's so cheap.'	That's because it's a dump.

STRESSED ERIC

France

For:	Against:
Dazzling culture, wine, food, l'atmosphere	Monsieur Smartarse, who pretends he can't understand you when you're really trying to make yourself understood in French (your accent is good and you haven't said 'tu' when you should have said 'vous') and he probably could understand you – in fact, of course he can, but he can't be bothered. He'd rather do that puzzled face and have a little shrug and leave you stuck in the middle of the Rue des Prostitutes looking like you've just won Sad Tourist of the Year.

Australia

For:	Against:
Stunning scenery – breathtaking mountain ranges, deserts, coastline.	Full of Australians.

Greece

For:	Against:
Stunning scenery – breathtaking mountain ranges, deserts, coastline.	Full of Greeks.

Spain

For:	Against:
Stunning scenery – breathtaking mountain ranges, deserts, coastline.	Full of English people.

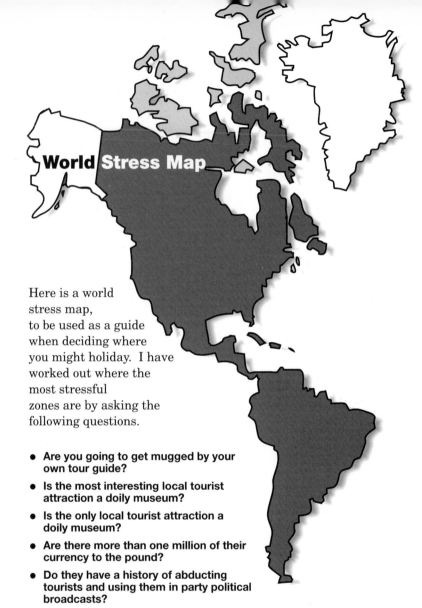

World Stress Map

Here is a world
stress map,
to be used as a guide
when deciding where
you might holiday. I have
worked out where the
most stressful
zones are by asking the
following questions.

- Are you going to get mugged by your own tour guide?
- Is the most interesting local tourist attraction a doily museum?
- Is the only local tourist attraction a doily museum?
- Are there more than one million of their currency to the pound?
- Do they have a history of abducting tourists and using them in party political broadcasts?
- Does the local language use the same word for 'hospital' and 'abattoir'?
- Is male rape considered a laughing matter?
- Is there a night spot called 'Huge Party Disco Club'?
- Does the most popular make of car have less than four wheels?
- Are Marillion considered a must-see musical act?
- Is the death penalty not only enforced but wildly popular?
- Is it still possible to be run over by animals?

STRESSED ERIC

Category 1: ☐ **Stressful** – Alaska, Norway, Greenland, New Zealand

Category 2: ☐ **Highly stressful** – a small section of Canada, the northern part of Japan, the Channel Islands

Category 3: ■ **Time to go to hospital (double-check that it's not the abattoir)** – everywhere else in the world

Externalizing Stress

One of the worst things you can do if you're stressed is to keep your anxiety and anger bottled up inside. If you internalize stress, you're never going to get rid of it; instead, it'll simply turn into an ulcer, a skin complaint or a heart attack. Many therapists insist that stress must be expressed or externalized, and they encourage us to unleash our stress through words, movement, or imagination. The problem is that when you externalize one stress, the process of externalizing creates a new stress that takes its place and in some cases is twice as bad as the original stress. Here, I'm going to talk about some of the ways we can externalize stress and how they can be potentially more damaging than sitting in the corner of a party privately nurturing your anxieties along with a bottle of Martini.

Let Your Anger Out

By adopting one of the following faces, as a way of expressing your stress, you can release the pent-up energy and tension that is blighting your life.

However, you should be careful when and where you use these. I was unfortunate enough to find myself making these faces at what, on reflection, were probably the wrong occasions, namely the funeral of a distant cousin, on a packed tube train (someone got so alarmed they pulled the communication cord), and the school sports day (to be fair, Brian had at that moment still not left the start line in the sack race and Heather Perfect was doing her lap of honour).

My experiences point up the flaw in this particular therapy – the very moments when you want to let your anger out are the moments when you can't, at least not without risking social embarrassment and even, on occasion, arrest.

STRESSED
ERIC

Art Therapy

Art therapy is another very popular way of externalizing stress. The theory is that by expressing all your rage and fear in the form of drawings and paintings, you can exorcize anxieties. I had high hopes for art therapy, but as I soon found out, it requires a sympathetic and caring teacher, not the belligerent old trout I found at the New Park College of Art. Mrs Doveday is the kind of woman of whom it could be said: those who can, do; those who can't, teach; those who can't even teach, teach art therapy at the New Park College of Art.

Here is my first set of paintings.

HMS Dunbar

HMS Exeter

HMS Bolton

HMS Belfast

At this point, Mrs Doveday tried to persuade me to leave behind the warships and go with something else. When I responded that I couldn't draw anything else, she said that was the whole point – to try what you couldn't do. I said, well that's a bit like going down the Cresta Run when you've never been in a toboggan. She ignored me completely and insisted that I start by taking some Old Masters as inspiration. By this point, I was in a particularly bloody-minded mood, so I dug my heels in. The results are displayed over the next few pages. On presentation of these, I was asked to leave the New Park Single Parent Art Therapy Group and never return.

A Sunday Afternoon on the Island of La Grande Jatte

The Creation of Adam

STRESSED
ERIC

Dance Therapy

For centuries, communities all over the world have used dance as a way of reducing tensions and stresses. The sheer joy and vitality of dance is, we are told, enough to liberate the spirit and it is also very good physical exercise which loosens and relaxes tense muscles. In my limited experience (one visit to the Honor Oak Park Royal British Legion Tea Dance) it is also frightening, intimidating and as much fun as a charity root canalathon.

On arriving, the first thing I had to do was find a partner. In my previous experience, finding a partner has never been easy. At school discos, all the girls wanted to dance with Ricky Wattis because he was handsome, tough and extremely unlikely to get any O levels (curiously this made him more attractive). Consequently, I was always left with the choice of either not dancing at all or dancing on my own but near a girl in the hope that once every few bars it might look like I was dancing *with* her. At the Tea Dance, though, I had the opposite problem. I was virtually mobbed the moment I walked through the door. Now, while I could flatter myself that common sense has finally prevailed upon the world and thin, plain-looking men with a lot of O levels are finally considered sex symbols, I have to admit it's probably because I was the only one under 70.

As the male of the couple, you are supposed to lead and guide your partner firmly and confidently through the steps. However, trying to lead Mrs Joy Sculthorpe in the tango was like trying to row the *Queen Mary* through a sea of Mars bars. No matter how hard I tried to twist and turn her, she obstinately refused to raise anchor and I was forced to sort of circle her, repositioning my hands every few steps so as not to break her arms off.

My second partner was even worse. Irene 'Panzer' Peterson was well named by the old blokes who regularly attend (and who I could see laughing at me over Ms Peterson's shoulder during the foxtrot). She was the one who was determined to lead, and given her bulk, her tenacity and the largest hands I've ever seen outside Russian shot-putting circles, I was in no position to argue.

In the course of the afternoon, we did a fraught and fractious rumba, during which she dead-legged me three times, an argumentative jitterbug, where she actually slapped me across the face for failing to lift her, and a terrifying swing jive, where she twirled me so vigorously that I cannoned into Major Derek Wilkes (MC, DSO), bounced off him into Reg and Mavis Swinnerton, and came to rest prone over the turntables of Mike Samson's Supersounds.

One final word of warning: there are many manuals on the market which teach you how to do ballroom dancing. Beware. They are hot on the theory but take very little notice of the practice. Here is a page from *A Beginner's Guide to Ballroom Dancing,* which I used to learn some steps. It is followed by a diagram of what actually took place when I attempted the same dance with the Panzer.

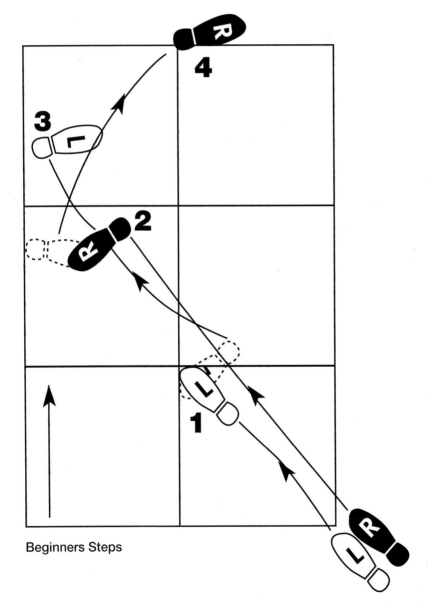

Beginners Steps

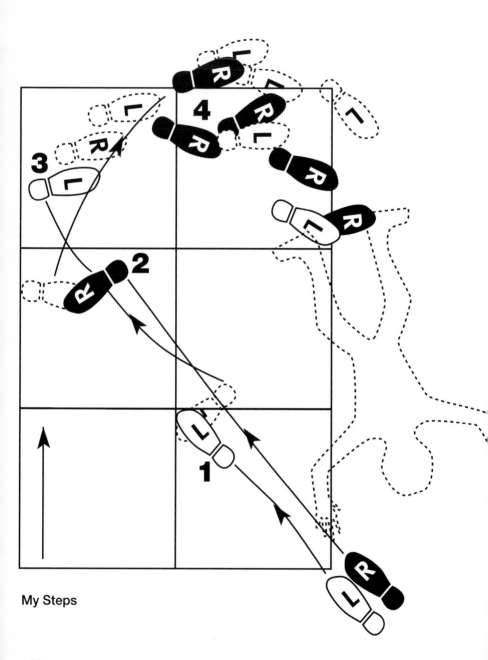

My Steps

STRESSED ERIC

Other Dances To Avoid

Ballet
Remember that moment when you last stubbed your toe against the wardrobe at home? Ballet is having the same feeling all the time while wearing tights and a dress.

Disco
You have two options with disco dancing. You can either jig around aimlessly, shuffling from side to side looking embarrassed, or you can go for it and pretend you're in *Saturday Night Fever*. Either way, you'll get beaten to a pulp by a gang of lads from Billericay.

Barn Dancing
The great advantage of barn dancing is that it's terribly easy. The great disadvantage of barn dancing is that it's only done by very thick people. You do the same thing over and over again and the person next to you still keeps trying to do-si-do when you should be forming a basket.

Morris Dancing
It would be okay to do this if you could do it exclusively in private, but you can't. Since it seems to take place outside pubs, it's likely that the people who are watching you will have had a skinful and will barely remember anything the next day. But the risk is too high. If even one pissed punter recalls seeing you and a lot of men in beards skipping around waving handkerchiefs, then your life's over.

Modern Dance
You can learn modern dance by spending four years at the Ballet Rambert School, exploring how to break with the conventions of formal steps, pre-ordained choreography and traditional notions of rhythm. Or you can produce the same results more quickly by drinking three bottles of cider and running up a down escalator.

Irish Dancing
Pointless and stupid. I mean, how did it begin? Somebody must have said, 'I know, let's do a dance where you can't move your arms,' and an entire nation said, 'Yeah!'

Line Dancing
Must have been invented by someone who didn't like dancing at all, but preferred sitting in a chair occasionally flicking his ankles from side to side. The only good reason to do this is that you can watch television and eat at the same time.

Drama Therapy

Drama therapy is also known as psychodrama and is a pioneering technique that enables people to re-enact traumatic events from their past as a means of coming to terms with them.

I went to the local drama therapy group having been assured I would find a warm and supportive environment in which to re-examine some of my formative bad moments. At school I suffered at the hands of Ricky Wattis, the school bully, and felt that if I were to replay one particular incident, it might help me to overcome the stresses and fears that have stayed with me ever since. Even to this day, I can't watch some of the meatier episodes of *Grange Hill* without a rising tide of panic. So David Uncton (a 35-year-old administrative assistant at the Ministry of Agriculture) was given the role of Ricky Wattis and instructed to bully me – but this time, I would be able to tell the bully exactly what I thought of him and thus prevent the bullying from denting my self-esteem. Here is what happened:

Ricky: *You're a prat, Feeble.*

Me: *I'm not actually.*

Ricky: *Yes, you are. You're a pathetic little squirt and I'm going to beat the living daylights out of you.*

Me: *You should know that I'm not going to take any notice of this childish taunting.*

Ricky: *That's 'cause you're a prat who's about to get his face smashed in.*

Me: *Actually, it's because I'm not afraid of you. You may be captain of the school rugby team, but I've got more O levels than you've had hot dinners.*

At this point Ricky punched me, cheered on by the rest of the group, who started to chant, 'Rick-ee, Rick-ee, Rick-ee.' The therapist in charge then called a halt to proceedings and we spent several hours examining why everyone instinctively sided with Ricky.

In conclusion, rather than exorcizing this horrible event, I found myself reliving it in gruesome detail with the now added trauma of having been physically set upon by a 35-year-old man I'd never met before, egged on by a baying mob. My conclusion is that, like white socks and fondues, drama therapy should be avoided at all costs.

STRESSED
ERIC

Visualization Therapy

In visualization therapy the aim is to relieve stress through the power of imagination. You are asked to picture mentally whatever it is that is causing stress or tension, and then to fantasize how you would like to deal with it. So, for example, if you have a fear of water, you might visualize yourself swimming in the sea, relaxed and happy. Thus, through imagination, you can prove to yourself that there is a way of coping with your particular problem.

Here, is a picture of one of the most stressful things in my life:

Now I'm going to visualize a number of ways in which I could deal with her.

Maria

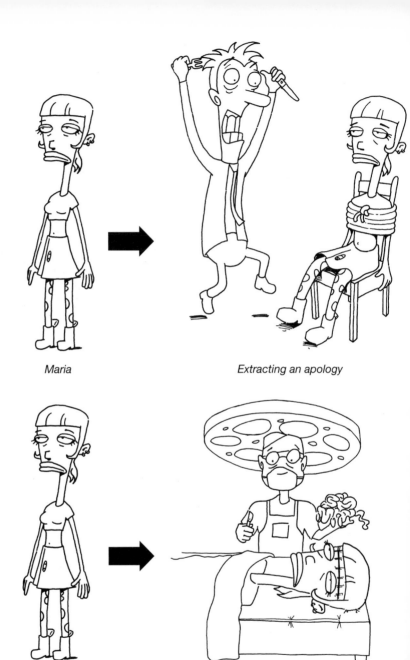

Maria

Extracting an apology

Maria

Lobotomy

STRESSED ERIC

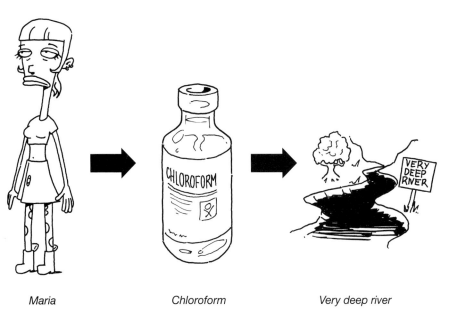

Maria   Chloroform   Very deep river

Having done this, I should feel much better about Maria, since I have mentally mapped out a series of alternatives for dealing with her, thus proving to myself that she is not an insurmountable problem. However, in reality, I feel much worse because none of these is actually a practical way of dealing with the situation. Though I absolutely, genuinely, unreservedly feel like doing these things, sometimes as many as 10 times a day (especially the last one – that sometimes keeps me awake at night, chuckling) they are obviously just fantasies. I'll never be able to realize them, and having had a tantalizing glimpse of this world, I'm now feeling more stressed than I did before I tried the visualization.

Conclusion
Far from liberating you from the constraints of stress, visualization is more frustrating than watching your Auntie Pam trying to set the video.

Let's have fun with Stress

It's well known that laughter is cathartic and a good laugh makes everyone feel better (that is, as long as it's not hysterical laughter born out of desperation – the sort I experienced last Tuesday when the announcer at the railway station declared, after a three-hour delay, that someone had actually stolen the points at Chatham). Laughter relaxes the body, calms the mind and restores that elusive thing called perspective. I thought I would devote a section to the amusing side of stress because, to be honest, at this point I'm so stressed by having to write this book that I need all the help I can get.

Games and Pastimes for the Stressed

Stressed-out Hangman

Hangman is a simple game. Admittedly, it sometimes gets bogged down in ferocious arguments about how to construct the gallows, but this should not hold things up for longer than a couple of hours. I recently enjoyed a thoroughly relaxing game with my friend the Doc (though both of us were slightly alarmed afterwards when we pondered the results of our game). Judge for yourself how successful the game was in taking my mind off my predicament.

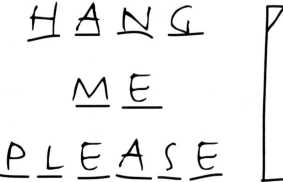 

STRESSED ERIC

Noughts and Crosses

This is another game that is supposedly simple enough to require little effort, yet interesting enough to be absorbing and de-stressing. However, I would advise you to approach the game with caution. I recently played a whole series of games of noughts and crosses with my daughter, Claire, on the train from London Bridge to Broadstairs. Every single game ended in a draw. As a result, I was so tense by the time we got to Broadstairs that when we passed a busking tap dancer, I didn't lob him 10 pence, I threw it with such force that it bounced up off the pavement in front of him and cut him across the bridge of the nose.

Here is a selection of some of our games:

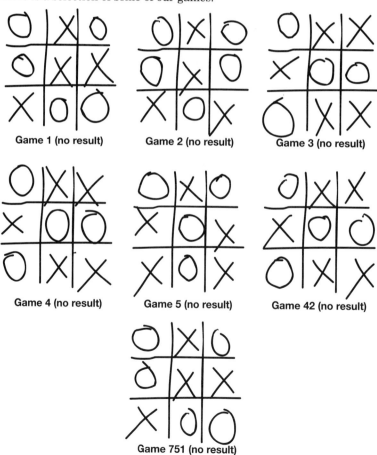

Game 1 (no result)   Game 2 (no result)   Game 3 (no result)

Game 4 (no result)   Game 5 (no result)   Game 42 (no result)

Game 751 (no result)

Crossword Puzzles

A crossword puzzle is an absorbing and interesting pastime that can unite the whole family. Last week, I tried to do the quick crossword in the paper with Claire and Brian. Here is what happened:

> **Me:** 1 across. 'Railway station in London (6).'
>
> **Claire:** 27 down is rabbit.
>
> **Me:** We're not doing 27 down, we're doing 1 across. 'Railway station in –'
>
> **Claire:** But 27 down is rabbit, and look, 24 across is umbrella.
>
> **Me:** You shouldn't be looking at either 27 or 24. We're doing 1 across.
>
> **Claire:** But I know what they are. And 25 across is –
>
> **Me:** CLAIRE! IT'S MY PAPER. I'M IN CHARGE. WE'RE DOING 1 ACROSS!

At this point Claire started to cry.

> **Me:** Oh, Claire, I'm so sorry.
>
> **Claire:** I hate you, you're horrid.

Claire ran upstairs and barricaded herself in her room. I then noticed that Brian had written his name in 5 down.

> **Me:** BRIAN, WHAT ARE YOU DOING? THE CLUE TO 5 DOWN IS 'GERMAN COMPOSER (9)'. HOW IS THE ANSWER TO THAT 'BRIAN'?

There was a pause. Then Brian started to cry, ran upstairs and barricaded himself in his room.

There was another pause. Then I started to cry, ran upstairs, and barricaded myself in my room.

STRESSED ERIC

Charades

Crosswords are clearly not advisable. Perhaps a better alternative is to try a party game. Charades, for example, is widely considered to be enjoyable, humorous and de-stressing. It's a chance to let your hair down, to have a laugh, and to pit your wits against your friends in an unpressurized and relaxed environment. In short, charades is fun. However, I have to say I've never been involved in a fun game of charades. In fact, in the fun stakes, I'd say it comes somewhere between sinusitis and erecting a new garden shed.

Firstly, there's the problem of which team you find yourself on. Only recently, I was invited round to the Perfects' next door for a game of charades and found myself in the kind of team that is so crap it can't even decide who should be the captain. There was a middle-aged woman who spent the whole evening saying that she was no good at games, and an extremely vocal and enthusiastic man of about 40, who had clearly never read a book, never seen a film and only ever watched the television programme *Crimewatch*, which was his answer to everything. (Even when I had made it abundantly clear that it was three words and we'd established that it was a film called *The Longest Something*, he insisted on shouting out *Crimewatch*.)

Secondly, in playing charades it seems that one team has all the luck and the other has none – there's nothing in between. At one point, my team had a run of *Daniel Deronda*, *The Love Song of J. Alfred Prufrock* and Winston Churchill's *History of the English-speaking Peoples,* while the Perfects' team got *Help*, *Neighbours* and *The Third Man*.

By the end of the evening, my team's confidence was at such a low ebb that, while the rival team were guessing correctly, celebrating wildly and, in Ray Perfect's case, making a rather bad taste triumphalist gesture in my direction, we were still struggling to establish whether it was a book or a film. I left the Perfects' house feeling a little like I'd spent the evening in a tumble-drier. In all honesty, I can't really recommend charades as anything other than a humiliating punishment for someone you don't really like.

Community Singing

Nothing lifts the spirits like a good old sing-song, where everyone gathers round the piano and takes it in turns to lead the others in a rousing chorus of everyone's favourite songs. In reality, though, this rarely happens.

First of all, you have to find a pianist. The good ones are sniffy about playing something simple (which is the kind of thing everyone can sing), while the crap ones are willing to play anything, but it's almost impossible to tell what it is. After this, you have to decide what you're going to sing. This takes at least three and a half hours. It's never helped by the fact that every piano stool in Britain contains the same paltry collection of tattered sheet music, including at least one Simon and Garfunkel song, The Moonlight Sonata Made Easy and 'Kumbaya'.

In the midst of this turmoil, what tends to happen is that the Person Who's Had The Singing Lessons takes over and suggests with complete false modesty that they 'have a go' at something, while everyone else is deciding what to sing. They then launch into something very long, very loud and very complicated (including trills, long sustained notes involving circular breathing, and a vibrato so wide that you could park a truck down the middle). Not content with having performed brilliantly, the Person Who's Had The Singing Lessons rubs it in by suggesting, completely disingenuously, that you do a number: 'You've heard enough from me.' This puts you in a real quandary – if you don't do something, you're a spoilsport, and if you do, you know you're committing the musical equivalent of hara-kiri.

So, you launch into the theme from the Monkees, speeding through the verse because you hope everyone will join in on the chorus. But they don't because they know you've fallen into that other fatal trap of Starting Too High, and they're not going to damage their vocal cords just to keep up with you. The only sound that emanates from the assembled company is the sound of the Person Who's Had The Singing Lessons, having roundly humiliated you, reinforcing it by rifling through the sheet music looking for their next number and loudly discussing the possibilities with their near neighbour.

Thankfully, you forget the words to the second verse and have to stop, and everyone else, seeing this as a chance to curtail your efforts, suddenly bursts into hysterical applause. There is a half-hearted attempt to find another singer (but nobody volunteers because they've seen what fate befalls someone foolish enough to try) before all eyes turn back to the Person Who's Had The Singing Lessons, who spends three minutes protesting, 'No, someone else, you don't want to hear me again, why doesn't Fran have a go?' before launching into the entire score of Sondheim's *Follies*.

People slowly drift away during 'Broadway Baby'. It's now half past midnight and the only person who's had a good sing-song is the Person Who's Had The Singing Lessons. What's worse is that your performance has lowered people's opinion of you to such an extent that most of them are unable to look you in the eye when they say good-night.

Board Games at Christmas

In most families, board games are given as presents at Christmas. The mistaken idea is that this will give the whole family something to enjoy, but, as my experience shows, in reality, it's the equivalent of wrapping up a hand grenade without the pin. Here are some of the stressful things about playing a new board game at Christmas.

1. Understanding the board game.
You have to pick your way through a set of rules so tortuous they could have been drawn up by a European Commission. You start reading aloud confidently: 'The object of the game is...' but when you still haven't got to the end of that sentence 15 minutes later, your confidence starts to evaporate.

2. Having to play with your children.
Your natural competitive instincts dictate that you want to flatten anyone in your path. But as a parent, you realize that if your children lose, your life won't be worth living until the following Christmas. On the other hand, if they realize that you're losing deliberately, this will also provoke floods of tears because you're not playing properly and your life won't be worth living till the Christmas after that.

3. Knocking over the board.
This tends to occur when everyone's a little overtired and overwrought, probably after about five hours of playing the game. Sod's law also dictates that it occurs when the board game is of the complicated variety, where whole cities have been built, consisting of towering edifices constructed of unstable plastic bits oh so carefully placed on specific squares. In the midst of an argument someone will accidentally knock the whole thing flying and you will then have to spend a day and a half arguing about where the bits were when you knocked the board over.

4. Deciding you've been playing it wrong.
This hideous discovery usually comes when you're trying to put the board back together after it's been knocked over. While most of the players are bickering, there's always one person who glances at the rules and has a Eureka moment, when they realize you've been playing the whole thing wrong from the start.

5. Becoming angry with the game.
This is the moment where, after interminable hours of torture, you approach the finish line, only to realize that the entire thing comes down to an absurd game of chance in which winning depends on being able to throw a double six. This discovery, coming as it does after much skilful and taxing brain play, makes you so furious with the manufacturers that you vow to put a brick through their window on the way to work on Monday morning.

Watching Television

Given that active family pursuits are clearly more likely to cause stress than assuage it, you may think it better to take your mind off your worries by spending time at home in a more passive way. Relaxing in front of the television seems ideal. Sitting on your sofa, you are whisked into any number of worlds where your stress is left behind. However, in my experience, your stress not only accompanies you, but it meets up with some of its friends. Here are some of the more stressful types of television.

1. Charity programmes where politicians try to prove they're good sports by being in sketches with Frank Bruno.

2. All children's programmes with hyperactive, kickable presenters.

3. Dull local news programmes, where the headlines start, 'Local primary school teachers in parking row'.

4. Documentaries that tell you something frightening about the place you live in (e.g. your house is built on a government testing site/volcano/former leper colony).

5. Tributes to dead comedians, where celebrities claim the comedian in question was fantastically funny but where the clips suggest they were about as funny as asthma.

Perhaps the most stressful thing about watching television is the remote control. Of course, this is supposed to make television watching even more relaxing on the basis that, with a remote, you don't even have to get up to change channel. In reality, however, having a remote control only causes more stress. Not only is it often harder to find than the lost world of Atlantis, but when you actually find it you're faced with an array of buttons that would confuse the Regius Professor of Button Technology at the University of Buttons.

STRESSED ERIC

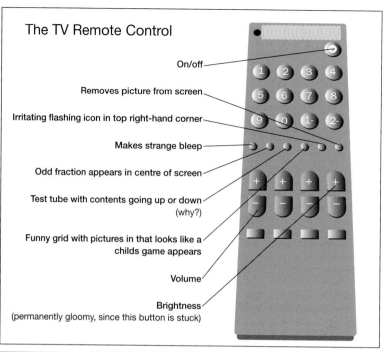

The TV Remote Control

On/off

Removes picture from screen

Irritating flashing icon in top right-hand corner

Makes strange bleep

Odd fraction appears in centre of screen

Test tube with contents going up or down (why?)

Funny grid with pictures in that looks like a childs game appears

Volume

Brightness
(permanently gloomy, since this button is stuck)

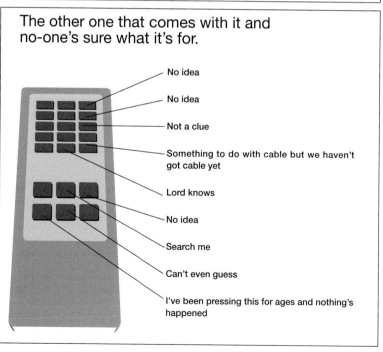

The other one that comes with it and no-one's sure what it's for.

No idea

No idea

Not a clue

Something to do with cable but we haven't got cable yet

Lord knows

No idea

Search me

Can't even guess

I've been pressing this for ages and nothing's happened

Cinema

Given that it's not really possible to avoid stress in your home, where can you go to escape, unwind and forget the annoyances and tensions that plague you? It's obvious – the cinema, the theatre of dreams, the doorway to romance and adventure. But while the film itself might lead you into this world of magic, the audience can just as quickly pull you back into the world of angina and tense neck muscles, as I discovered when I went to the local Odeon last week.

First, I found myself sitting in front of the cinema's resident running commentator. This was someone who seemed to feel it was helpful to describe in an irritating whisper everything that was happening on the screen to her friend:

> 'Oh, look, he's gone into the strongroom – oh, look, the policeman's gone in too – oh, look, he's got a gun.'

What was worse was that I then realized I was sitting behind someone who'd already seen the film and couldn't resist telling the person he was with what was coming up:

> 'He's going to murder that other bloke in a minute. 'Cause the thing is, he's not actually a policeman. He's the mastermind behind the whole robbery. But what's really clever is, you don't find that out until the very end.'

And to cap it all, I was sitting next to someone who would have found watching the Test Card a challenge:

> 'So why have they gone into the bank when it's closed? Oh, I see, it's a robbery. So who are they robbing?'

STRESSED
ERIC

Stressful Types of Film to be avoided at all costs

Stressful Film Type 1:
Kookie romantic comedies

These often involve short men who are supposed to make up for being unattractive by being funny (though that's a matter of opinion) and semi-attractive women who've usually got one outstandingly bad feature but make up for it by looking cutesy the whole time. The plots are always the same – they're best friends all the way through and then, after two hours of drivel, realize they should have been shagging all along.

'What I'm trying to say is I love you, you big dumb stupid bunch of klutz.'

Stressful Film Type 2:
Anything in that hard-bitten, postmodern,
flashy heroin-chic world mode.

Against a deafening soundtrack by a useless group called the Testicles,
people with impenetrable Scottish accents swear a lot, stab each other
and disappear down toilets. There is no plot, no substance and no point
and loads of students come out of the cinema afterwards gushing,
'Oooh, it's so visceral.'

Bottle me, love me, slash me,
pick me up on a razor blade,
shame me with your
SHITE SHITE SHITE

*'Fggn yuw Mackies nae gonna go Jimmy fuss wi a stottie, I's nae cm back.
Whees Mack, noooo, hee's back wid thee heed ya farck.'*

STRESSED
ERIC

Stressful Film Type 3:
Anything that involves
Keanu Reeves trying to act

'I'm the top defence counsel in the country.'

Going to the Theatre

For centuries the theatre has been considered a cathartic experience that alleviates stress. Aristotle himself believed that there was nothing like a good tragedy for taking your mind off things, but then Aristotle didn't have to spend the best part of a year's salary to actually get seats. According to the dictionary, catharsis is 'a relief of strong feelings or tensions by giving vent to them in drama'. But what is so frequently overlooked is the strong feelings and tensions that are produced by a night in the West End.

For instance, on many occasions your seat has something known as a restricted view. This means that although you've paid £28 for your ticket, there is a small wall in front of your seat. The only action you can see on the stage is the bit reflected in the spectacles of the person sitting behind you. Of course, you do have opera glasses, which in this case are essential if you're to see what's going on in the spectacles of the person sitting behind you, but getting them out without ripping the back off the seat in front is a virtual impossibility.

When the play actually begins, you're hit with the terrible realization that the entire play is dependent on the deployment of accurate accents and none of the actors in the cast is capable of providing them. It's a toss-up which is worse: English actors doing American accents or American actors doing English accents. Either way, they're probably both topped by posh actors doing Cockney accents. In fact, the only thing that gets you through the first half is the thought of being able to down some alcohol in the interval. Unfortunately, you're then faced with an even more stressful problem: namely, trying to find out on which continent your interval drinks have been hidden.

The second half brings no respite. The crap accents have ceased to be funny, and hunger as well as thirst is beginning to bite. You're even reduced to that most desperate of hopes when you're in the theatre: that a piece of scenery will collapse or that – please God – the leading actor will have a highly visible and therefore amusing erection.

In conclusion, a less stressful and more enjoyable alternative would be to take £100 out of the bank, rip it up, then lock yourself in a wardrobe with Dick van Dyke.

Listening to Music

Listening to music is a sure-fire way of reducing stress. What could be more restful than lying back, closing your eyes and letting soothing sounds wash over you, chasing away the troubles of the day? This does, however, depend on one key element, namely, having soothing music to listen to.

When Liz and I divorced, she took most of the record collection with her, and, as a consequence, my listening possibilities, as far as de-stressing goes, were not so much curtailed as liquidized. Here is a complete list of my record collection. What would you pick to help you relax?

Deep Purple, *Made in Japan*
Deep Purple, *Machine Head*
Lynyrd Skynyrd, *Freebird*
Bruce Springsteen, *Born in the USA*
The Russian Red Army Choir, *Kalinka!*
Richie Blackmore's Rainbow, *Rainbow Rising*
Great War Movie Themes
Emerson, Lake and Palmer, *Brain Salad Surgery*
Emerson, Lake and Palmer, *Tarkus*
Jon Hiseman's Colisseum II, *Strange New Flesh*
Led Zeppelin IV
King Crimson, *Starless and Bible Black*
Judas Priest, *Ram It Down*
Soundtrack from Platoon
Sex Pistols, *Never Mind the Bollocks*
The Jam, *Greatest Hits*
Zigger Zagger: *A Collection of Football Chants*
Budgie, *Never Turn Your Back on a Friend*
Robin Trower, *Bridge of Sighs*
Bad Company, *Straight Shooter*
Hawkwind, *Silver Machine*
Barry White, *Greatest Hits (cover only, record missing)*
Jimi Hendrix, *Greatest Hits*
Nazareth, *Expect No Mercy*
The Sensational Alex Harvey Band, *Live*
Beethoven, *Pastoral Symphony*

Now, the obvious choice is the last one – Beethoven's Pastoral Symphony is one of the most soothing pieces ever written. However, the reason Liz left this LP is that it's got a huge scratch on it. Consequently, although the music is very calming, it's impossible to listen to because you're tensely awaiting the arrival of the scratch and asking those searching questions: What's it going to do today? Is it going to leap into the middle of the next movement with a horrible crack? Or is it going to get stuck so I have to give the needle a push, sending it bouncing across the rest of the record and adding another couple of deep furrows?

Relaxation Techniques

Most stress manuals are full of simple relaxation exercises, which are non-strenuous and designed to help you achieve inner peace. The most popular of these is meditation, where you sit quietly and empty your mind.

Emptying one's mind is a very difficult task, of course, so one's advised to pick a simple object and concentrate entirely on it. I chose the bookshelf. This was a mistake. I soon noticed that my copy of *Eddie Condon: A Life in Jazz* was missing, and I remembered that Brian had taken it to school for a project on the 1920s and had obviously not returned it. This, in turn, reminded me that I'd also given him *The Louise Brooks Story* and my favourite pen and I began to resent all the things that over the years I've given to my kids and which have disappeared into a black hole. By this point, I wasn't really thinking about the shelf at all. I was thinking about my total failure as a parent to raise my kids to be responsible and respectful of other people's property, particularly mine. This then spiralled into a much deeper, darker reflection on my total failure as a parent per se and wondering whether I'd succeeded in adult life in any way at home, at work, or in any social or familial context. I came to the awful conclusion that I had failed, that my whole life was pointless, and I began to play that game of best death, when you imagine how you would prefer to pass into the next life. Thankfully, at this point I was woken from my reverie by the sound of the telephone. Gratefully, I answered it. It was someone from work asking if he could borrow my copy of *Eddie Condon: A Life in Jazz*. I think he was rather bemused when I swore at him and slammed the phone down.

Since meditation didn't really help me, I have devised an alternative relaxation technique which I found much more beneficial.

STRESSED ERIC

Eric Feeble's Practical Guide to Relaxing

Exercise 1

1. Clear your living room wall of any obstacle.
2. Find a glass ashtray.
3. Take the ashtray in your right hand.
4. Adopt a comfortable standing position, legs slightly apart, about 2 feet from the wall.
5. Breathe deeply.
6. Close your eyes.
7. Count to ten.
8. Open your eyes.
9. Smash the ashtray against the wall.

Exercise 2

1. Clear your living room floor of any obstacle.
2. Find a glass ashtray.
3. Take the ashtray in your left hand.
4. Adopt a comfortable sitting position, legs extended.
5. Breathe deeply.
6. Close your eyes.
7. Count to ten.
8. Open your eyes.
9. Smash the ashtray against the floor.

Exercise 3

1. Clear your patio of any obstacle.
2. Find a glass ashtray.
3. Take the ashtray in both hands.
4. Adopt a comfortable kneeling position.
5. Breathe deeply.
6. Close your eyes.
7. Count to ten.
8. Open your eyes.
9. Smash the ashtray against the patio.

I have found all these exercises to be helpful in the relief of stress. Alternatives include smashing the ashtray against the washing-machine, the window and the au pair.

Medical Help for the Stressed

Another way of dealing with stress is to take drugs of various sorts: anti-depressants, relaxants, tranquillizers and so forth. This is a very controversial topic, since many people believe that conditions such as stress and anxiety should not be dealt with by chemical means. My view is that drugs can be helpful for the stressed (and if you'd ever been stuck in a traffic jam on the A11 with your daughter screaming that she wants to go to the loo and your son screaming that he's actually going, you'd want to down anything you could get your hands on). So here is a balanced resumé of the arguments for and against drug intervention in dealing with stress.

Against	For
Drugs are expensive.	But so is going to the theatre, and drugs are a lot more rewarding.
Drugs are bad because they take us away from natural organic healing processes.	Which means having some lisping vegan shove his hand up your rectum to massage your colon – more drugs please.
Drugs can severely affect your personality, turning you into a smiling zombie.	As opposed to an unsmiling one.
Coming off drugs can be difficult.	So don't try.
Drugs represent an easy solution.	And your point is?

STRESSED ERIC

I can vouch for the fact that drugs can help with stress. My friend the Doc has, on numerous occasions, prescribed me various drugs, including the following:

Truzambuterol, Ambuterol, Quadrambuterol, Clairlatsmastine, Zanthamine, Cycandol, Morphocycandol, Bitridizanthiagrene, Zumalum, Picanol, Antihistathine, Bizamborderol, Pantagrene, Anti-dibihisterine, Quantomel, Phenogerol, Morbancondine, Xymantherol, Hesteron, Dapthon, Santagyl, Diazemine, Diazemine-antinodrexol, Promanterene, Prophenongerol, Zustanenthenerol, Xistigol, Phandangerine, Phanomene, Anti-phanomene, Xeestohepthamerol, Quordine, Anti-lygo, Desinnol, Comquanderine, Fumalene, Frangerate, Dispandepsimine, Peptopterate, Dessteranzepthenerol, Corgrantuine, Poostiheptamine, Vydan, Zapthon, Apsro-zapthon, Canerostenol, Visdanitzaptherol, Ponteluene, Kyzemanantimodrexolbeanthropol, Cynol, Bitransbuterolmathepteronalene, Wiseapbelon, Xanthbapterol, Xanthopateomol, Histepteroxelon, Kistafurantomene, Zlobodanephandemol, Koalamene, Dasoll, Heptoquerolodiphibolomene, Estamene, Dispopterol, Federopofite, Obzataveld, Exomene, Chrustopheneme, Phangolophite, Ditriphangolophite, Fungamene, Dittotriptiathemine, Xasqat, Extrohunterol, Buphathine, Hoosgatanteophiascathine, Helmadrine, Zospat, Klungathickeron, Korpelderate, Holdrup, Hugepatantioogrobdignag, Disconpholetiquateronolethemene, Lickothonantiputz, Dickanol, Combarseate, Bicombarseate, Dicombarseate, Vageomaterol, Reptogevorate, Arsfaciocrombol, Vagerate, Scubblium, Bendit, Dickiwissel, Hobbishooio, Contrabuggerate, Brand-headedthumpthrom, Wombit, Spongum, Dunkum, Squigglum, Vascobieterolansiditerolkrystanthemusiatilexterolphiagitate, Aspirin, Bullum, Xasteronthopo-lampoopoodum, Squellum, Phenosquellerate, Xybasanthrogridlum, Vassal, Contraphol, Rimcacaselum, Excretolium, Pisserine, Digobberol, Lyingandethenerol, Moscatelium, Antidesoconnorine, Wyzzum, Chillum, Darkumthrobbum, Jizzerol, Whosbletted, Bilioscorate, Antivallumdullum, Hypzerine, Peniserium, Mingerine, Logsummerene, Dartboardum, Vakynol, Novakynol, Trivakonyl, Escaperol, Rolorol, Pholorol, Pholorolderol, Phalaladedrol, Hebben, Cummabum, Summacummabum, Dyspepserol, Dassenzene, Bideham, Gribblene, Bindehamtrigribblemedithexol, Zanodarsus, Mephthpholerate, Quondisberanderene, Duckfrot, Gynearol, Gynepigerol, Obserat, Xamonotherol, Vestamathanthropolethylvitaxilatet, Hapthopcrustamene, Lum, nackathon, Nyphaterol, Nansoatheolphendacterol, Scuzzateorol, Scrotterene, Ubthorpdandephyle, Wrexhamene, Whosdatophyl, Mindmebumathene, Scuffalottachipsene, Rubenerol, Climatfunderene, Schipsal, Wundaschipsal, Dattewagenereothron, Wupsupdene, Returnerol, Phengetol, Klatterol, Shrubsenantimogaterol, Blokerol, Ruddesmene, Biatapholdispendrigate, Labiolum, Tuckersmol, Diphenderyl, Landelum, Ickywickythol, Skulardeneserum, Phickmatchplayhorsenum, Lobmedownum, Sickol, Phungmedustrum, Lickiturdismadum, Poolampedol, Cyclopswussmedearum, Crunchmewattel, Jackum, Jisanthroporliamanthrate, Sodium Punchium, Bitriquadriquintoheptomonoprophenolapterol, Bardrumasol, Bizaminoheptowatalotacorum, Desdrementharene, Squalarotheron, Listamine, Mistamine, Nistamine, Pistamine, Queegeranathol, Ziamessionbanthroglamanate, Hastemenioanthroporlum, Bumzol, Xystolibium, Quickzoxacanol, Quickzopessanol, Xyscatum, Scatulottum, Crapperol, Crumzadrenohippanol, Vestalum, Parterene, Scunthalenobiderol, Pescadrosaminozam, Lustarium, Vistalinambinozolarium, Quexolodram, Xampordolamanothine, Dreckanol, Bescalumbizamadrol, Coliamadrine, Derinarsusaminerol, Ephanosympilanoampinosaganol, Grexalamathene, Idolysum, Antrextolate, Willenathol, Quiatalum, Carbencherate, Zymonarsus, Antigotimonol, Volumsatiotatum, Mogaderol, Gribatrine, Sacalene, Bizedrinantimozecanol, Zustanolantimodecanol, Morphosecanol, Xuscatemptomine, Licmidinnathon, Chuzamberol, Vitanapserol, Hepteranagrat, Stickivasterol, Lubsenograt, Hestiophenolambuterine.

The Doc Says:

When Eric first turned up at my surgery he was tighter than a pair of supermodel's pants on Fatima Whitbread. My advice to him was either get a new pair of pants or give up the javelin, by which I meant, something's gotta give and you don't want it to be your underwear (not unless you're trapped in a lift with an air hostess called Melons).

As you've already seen, we tried the drug route but that had more bumps in it than a cheerleader's T-shirt. So I thought I'd look for an alternative, something off the beaten thong. As I was leafing through the pages of *Playnurse*, I saw an advert for a flotation tank and it struck me that this might do the trick. I tried it out myself and, sure enough, it's the most fun thing I've done since nude wine-tasting.

How To Use a Flotation Tank

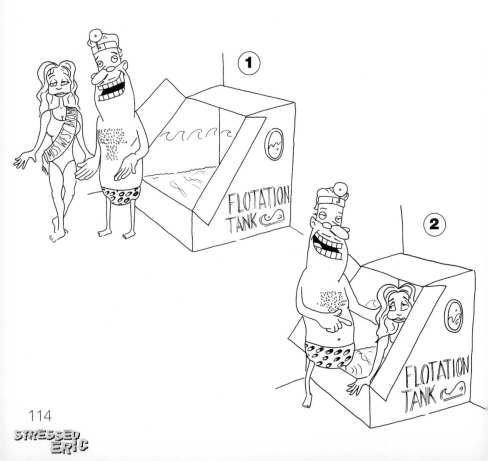

STRESSED
ERIC

Following Doc's advice I did indeed try the flotation tank, but my experience of it was rather different from his.

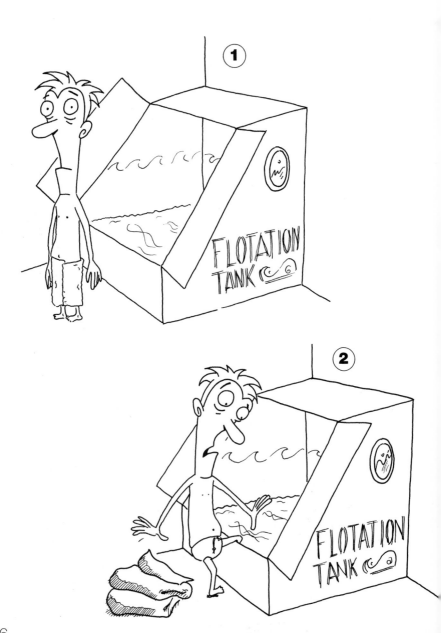

STRESSED ERIC

Spiritual Help for the Stressed

For many people, solace and help come from their spiritual and religious beliefs. No matter how wearisome and troubling the world of man, people with faith always find inner peace and fulfilment, and they will tell you that their religion helps them overcome anything, providing them with strength in the face of adversity and joy in the face of tragedy.

Now, it seems to me that if faith is going to help you, you have to pick the right one. I was raised a Roman Catholic, and rather than finding it helpful, it seems to me to be the most stressful religion ever invented. Here is a list of the five most stressful things about being a Catholic:

1. The guilt
2. The guilt
3. The guilt
4. The guilt
5. The guilt

Strictly speaking, I'm no longer a Catholic, since I lapsed about 20 years ago. Here is a list of the five most stressful things about being a lapsed Catholic:

1. The guilt
2. The guilt
3. The guilt
4. The guilt
5. The guilt

That's the trouble with Catholicism. You can never get away from the guilt. Even now, having been through Methodism, atheism, Buddhism and creationism, the only thing I'm really certain about is that I'm still guilty about not being a Catholic.

The reason that faith can help the stressed is that, whatever happens, you have someone to turn to in times of crisis, namely, God. The problem with this, as I have found over the years, is that it means believing in something you can't see. I have trouble believing my washing-machine will work next Tuesday and it's standing right in front of me, so how am I supposed to believe in an omnipotent, omnipresent, omniscient being who's never even been in my kitchen, and if he has, certainly never left a note? People tell me that this is what faith is, but my definition of faith is slightly more prosaic. For me, faith is believing that Brian will come back at the end of the school day with only his teeth and tongue in his mouth.

STRESSED
ERIC

One of the main reasons why religious people are so unstressed is that they always have something to look forward to, i.e. death. Death, they say, is something to be welcomed, a joyous event after which we shall all be gathered in the bosom of the Lord to live eternally in the afterlife. How anyone could find this an inspiring thought beats me. First, you've got to die. Now, I've rarely come across any completely relaxing ways of doing that. Most of them, it seems to me, involve enormous discomfort (long-term illness), major embarrassment (dying on the job) or both (accidents involving Miss Whiplash and some clingfilm come to mind). Then, once you're dead, the trouble really starts. What's eternity like? Do you get the same au pair? Do you have to live at the same address? Is your copy of *Eddie Condon: A Life in Jazz* still missing? Most things in life are bearable only because you think you're going to get through them and at some point they'll be over. But imagine being in a place where the only certainty is that everything's going to continue forever. What does that mean in terms of television repeats?

Of course, not every religion believes in an afterlife in quite the same way. Buddhism, for instance, teaches us that we are reincarnated and that we become a higher or lower life form according to how we have lived our previous life. This itself presents a number of extremely stressful problems. First, there's a much higher statistical chance that you'll come back as an ant (of which there are billions) than as the Sultan of Brunei (of which there's one, and someone's already taken it). And what if you come back as an animal you despise? I hate those yappy little Yorkshire terriers that their owners pass off as high-spirited, when in fact they're just mean-tempered little bastards. What kind of self-esteem problems would you have trotting round on all fours knowing you're the kind of creature that in your past life you would have liked to drop-kick into the next street?

This raises the issue of whether you're aware of your role in a previous life. As you romp around, crapping on pavements and pushing your nose into people's crotches, do you think, 'Blimey, I used to be Eric Feeble'? Certainly the people who believe in reincarnation talk about their awareness of past lives. But do you notice how they always seem to have had colourful and interesting lives as noblemen at the court of King Louis XIV or heroic soldiers in the Crimea? Strange, isn't it, that no one ever pipes up and says, 'You know, I used to be that type of plankton that eats its own poo'?

All in all, it's more relaxing to think that the only fate that awaits you is several million years of a very deep sort of sleep (but without the nightmares and having to get up to go to the loo).

Another kind of spiritual response to stress is to join a cult. Many people feel safe and protected by belonging to a cult, although this is perhaps a trifle over-optimistic given that most cults occasionally insist on mass suicide. It seems to me, however, that being in a cult would be more stressful than almost any other religious group. There you are, standing at Victoria Station, someone comes up to you and asks if you're happy, the next thing you know, you've been deprived of sleep for a week, you're dying for something to eat and you'll agree to anything, even marriage to a total stranger in a football stadium in Korea. And all you wanted to do was go and visit your auntie in Haslemere...

People also garner huge support from the great spiritual texts. They find that darkness is always lifted by a reading from the Psalms or the Gospels. In my experience, reading the Bible is a profoundly stressful experience. You're faced with choosing a version that veers between the absurdly old-fashioned and impenetrable (i.e. translated by an idiot king 400 years ago) or the ultra-modern version that tries to be hip (presumably translated by someone wearing a tie-dyed T-shirt and an inane grin). While the first of these, the King James version, ties itself up in knots ('And they did then go forth and thus supplicate lest they not be the ones that He had chosen for they were not the ones to enter the temple before the others'), the latter couldn't tie up its own shoelaces ('And the Lord said to the breadheads in the temple, "Hey, guys, get off my case"').

The subject matter of the Bible is also extremely stressful, involving wholesale slaughter, shocking plagues, child genocide and continual wall-to-wall, back-to-back, unmitigated sin. When Jesus arrives in the New Testament, it becomes slightly more cheerful, but things soon go horribly wrong again. We then get St Paul banging on about how terrible the human race is (as if we didn't already know) and how no one's allowed to do anything they want. It all culminates in Revelations, where the whole world turns into the set of *London's Burning*. If a film was ever made of the Bible, it wouldn't be rated 18, it would be rated 261.

STRESSED ERIC

Conclusion

So what have we learned? In the first section we saw how almost every aspect of modern life created unbearable stresses. In the second section we examined various ways of dealing with these stresses and saw how all of them failed, usually making things much worse. You might think that my conclusion is inevitably going to be pessimistic and depressing. In some ways, it is. Well, in quite a lot of ways. In fact, let's face it, you could find more optimism in the *Collected Works of Samuel Beckett*.

But, in spite of everything, I think there are rules we can follow which can help us in our stress-filled lives. Here is the Eric Feeble Five-point Plan to Countering Stress:

1. *Assume the worst at all times.*
   While things will still be worse than you imagined, it'll only be by a small margin. Never ever try to convince yourself that things are going to be great. If you do this, the gap between expectation and reality will be the size of Norway.

2. *Celebrate tiny victories.*
   You'd be amazed at how excited you can be the first time you assemble a barbecue.

3. *Take pleasure in other people's misfortunes.*
   It's surprising how satisfying this can be. All it takes is the sight of the Perfect family going down with flu to fill your life with sunshine.

4. *Sleep as much as possible.*
   While dreams can be very stressful (I'm thinking of one in particular where I was chased round John Lewis's by the Gestapo, the Spanish Inquisition and Mossad), at least they stop when you wake up.

5. *Avoid the following at all costs:*
   Portuguese au pairs, builders and all books on stress management (except this one). (Please buy this one – the deal I did on this was so bad that I got nothing up front, nothing on delivery of the manuscript and a royalty rate so poor that I have to sell more than 1,000,000 copies if I'm going to cover the cost of writing it.)

I hope this book is of some help to you. It should at least remind you that however stressful your life is, there's always someone worse off than you.
Me.

Yours stressfully

Eric Feeble

Appendix

Some Stress Lists

While I was researching and writing this book, I compiled the following lists dealing with other stressful areas of human experience. Originally, they were meant to be included in the text proper, but I found it impossibly stressful trying to fit them in, so here they are in one lumpen morass. Enjoy.

The five most stressful ways in which people have introduced themselves to me at dinner parties

1. Hi, my name's Mike. I'm a quantity surveyor.
2. Hi, I'm Angie. Don't tell me you're another Piscean!!!!!
3. My name's Isobel. I used to be Ian.
4. Hi, my name's Bob. As in '–a-job'! Ha ha ha ha ha ha!!
5. Hi, my name's Being. I don't believe in names.

The five most stressful singles of all time

1. 'I Love to Love', especially the bit when Tina Charles suddenly turns into a hyena.
2. 'Every Time You Go Away' by Paul Young. The chorus sounds like 'Every time you go away, you take a piece of meat with you'.
3. 'Hey Jude' by the Beatles. How can this be a classic when the last 10 minutes sound as if they were performed at the pub down the road?
4. 'A Whiter Shade of Pale' by Procol Harum. I don't even understand the title, let alone the song.
5. Anything that gets to number one in Turkey.

The five most stressful foods

1. Prunes – the smell.
2. Spaghetti – the mess.
3. Chocolate éclairs – the guilt.
4. Smoked salmon – the price.
5. Anything that takes longer to prepare than the time it takes to get the packet open.

STRESSED ERIC

The five most stressful things about being in a supermarket

1. When the old lady in front of you at the checkout utters those fateful words, 'No, hang on, I think I've got it all here in change.'
2. The moment on a packed Saturday morning, when your five-year-old asks you loudly, 'What is a vagina?'
3. Trying to work out how to unharness the trolleys without recourse to a blow torch.
4. You hope to bump into the person of your dreams, but instead you bump into Mandy Skingrove with whom it took you 20 seconds to lose your virginity.
5. Your son licks everything in the supermarket and you have to buy it all.

The five most stressful things about travelling by air

1. The bit in the emergency drill when they talk about crashing into the middle of the Atlantic ocean and being able to attract attention by blowing some poxy whistle.
2. Being sat on a flight to Australia between a teething child and a *Star Trek* fan.
3. Trying to wipe your bottom in turbulence.
4. Finding other people's ear wax in your head set.
5. Landing with Air Malta.

The five most stressful sights you will see in your life

1. Your parents having sex.
2. Your parents having sex with next door's parents.
3. Auntie Betty sitting on the toilet (she forgot to lock the door).
4. Whatever's left on your plate at the end of a Chinese meal.
5. Your father dancing to 'Oops Upside Your Head' at the Save the Children Fund Christmas Party.

The five most stressful things about being young

1. Having to go swimming in your pants because your mother's forgotten your trunks.
2. Having so little pocket money that the only purchasing decision you have to make is Rolo or Twix.
3. Having to go to bed when it's still light.
4. Having no teeth and looking like Orson Welles.
5. Only being able to find out that worms taste horrible by putting them in your mouth.

The five most stressful things that can happen at a funeral

1. During a cremation the fire goes out and someone has to ring for an electrician.
2. The corpse comes back to life during the playing of 'Morning Has Broken'.
3. You are pall-bearing and drop the coffin on the foot of the deceased's widow.
4. You get confused, think it's a wedding and turn up with some glasses and a matching decanter.
5. You are so embarrassed and English and don't know what to say to the deceased's parents that you blurt out something about wanting to remember him with laughter and how he once hilariously defecated into a paper cup on holiday in Majorca.

STRESSED ERIC

Further reading

If you've found this book useful, you might like to consult some of the following, which explore various aspects of stress and stress management in more detail.

Zweibel and Copman, *Stress*
Zweibel and Copman, *Stress Again*
Zweibel and Copman, *Superstress*
Zweibel and Copman, *Stress IV: Beyond Thunderdome*
Daniel Flashman, *After a Coronary*
Daniel Flashman, *Before a Coronary*
Daniel Flashman, *I'm Having a Coronary!*
Lucy Kroz, *One Hundred and Twelve Steps to Correct Breathing*
Hack Goulding, *Doddlism: A Way to Improved Health Through Doily-making*
Dwight Freem, *Aaaaaaaargh!*
Dwight Freem, *Waaaaaaaaaaaarrrrgggggghhhh!*
Dwight Freem, *Blooooooooooody Noooooooraaaaaaa!*
Blaydon Herscowitz, *Ha ha ha ha sob: Laughing with Stress*
Wolfgang Bleidenschrof, *Untergangenen bis Stressegefunken*
René le Faix, *Le Trauma psychique et le stresse d'aujourd'hui*
Jamie Lund, *Mend my Wok!: Stress and Aggression Among the Islington Set*
Nicky Pukker, *Unless You Come and Fix My Washing Machine Soon, the Boy Dies: The Dark Side of Stress*
Grace Nelderflower, *Zip-a-dee-doo-dah, zip-a-dee-stress: Relieving Stress Through Producing Musicals*
Herb Amontills, *Does Everyone's Baby Look Like Deng Xiao-ping? Stress and Parenting*
Walter Johnson, *The Operas of Strauss*
Chris Zeitman, *The Swollen Rabbit: Coping with Stress Through Taxidermy*
Herman Chantal, *I Love You Triton Power-shower Girl: Stress and Sexual Frustration*
Martha Weintraub, *Stress! Don't Talk to Me About Stress – You Should Try Living with Your Father, the Only Thing He's Given Me in Thirty Years Is Herpes: A Jewish Perspective on Stress*
A. Vasserheim, *Psychoanalytic Readings of Discursive Modes of Behaviour in Extremis Modandum with reference to Psychological Genderization and Other Psychodynamic Patterns of Classification*
Meg Watson, *The Join the Dots Stress Book*

Index

The publishers did ask me to provide a full and comprehensive index to help the user of this manual. Unfortunately, by the time I got to the end of the text, it was 7.30 on the morning I had to hand the manuscript in and Maria had just arrived home with the singer from the band Crushed Mothers. The singer gave my daughter, Claire, a copy of their new album Fallopian Steam Press, but she turned out to be allergic to the wrapping and she evacuated over the computer. Frantic attempts at reviving it having failed, I was forced to write the index very quickly by hand. If it seems a bit cursory, it wasn't my intention, but given the circumstances (on a number 53 bus coming into Trafalgar Square) it's the best I could do.

STRESSED ERIC

HEALTH, WEALTH AND HAPPINESS

by Ray Perfect

1,000,000 copies sold!

By the author of:

FANTASTIC, INCREDIBLE, SUPERB
ACHIEVEMENT, SUCCESS, FULFILMENT
HOORAY, HURRAH, ENCORE

**'One of the greatest prose
stylists of the century'**
Martin Amis

**'It's a triple-decker cheese and
bacon arseburger of a book'**
Paul Power

'Oh to be this funny'
John Cleese

**'It even works as a beautiful
object in its own right'**
Terence Conran

'It helped me walk again'
Sid Tunnock (paralysed victim of
parachuting accident)